D1621903

THE ASCENT OF LIFE

THE ASCENT OF LIFE

*A Philosophical Study
of the Theory of Evolution*

T. A. GOUDGE

*Professor of Philosophy
The University of Toronto*

UNIVERSITY OF TORONTO PRESS

PRINTED IN THE U.S.A.

PREFACE

This is an essay by a philosopher about present-day evolutionary theory. It is neither a popular survey of the history of life nor a technical contribution to biology. The developments which have occurred in the theory of evolution during the past few decades seem to me of the greatest philosophical interest and importance. Yet these developments have received very little attention from philosophers. I hope, therefore, that the present work, despite its limitations, will convince them that the subject is well worth pondering. I also hope that the work may appeal to biologists and general readers who have a taste for the philosophical discussion of scientific doctrines.

To conduct the discussion properly it has seemed to me essential to get down to biological details. Some may think that far too many such details have been introduced into a work which purports to be philosophical. But concerning this I am wholly impenitent. If a philosopher wants to talk about evolutionary theory, the least he can do is to examine it fairly closely and not be satisfied with a few vague impressions. On the other hand, since I do not claim to have any professional competence in biology, I have had to derive my knowledge of numerous particulars from the works listed in the bibliography. I am enormously indebted to the writings of Carter, Dobzhansky, Haldane, Huxley, Mayr, Muller, Simpson and Wright. It is not to be expected that in every instance I have got the details exactly right. Nor is it to be expected that biologists who disagree with the authors on whom I have relied will find all my statements acceptable. Efforts have been made, however, to report accurately what these authors have said; and some account of dissenting biological opinions has been taken at various points.

The philosophical questions discussed in the work are intended to be a representative sample, not an exhaustive catalogue. Each is treated so as to keep its discussion within reasonable limits. Consequently, no famous last words are said about any of them. One question in particular—what is the philosophical significance of the evolution of consciousness and self-consciousness in *Homo sapiens*?—opens up a subject so large and complex as to call for separate treatment on another occasion. Hence, although I have alluded to the question at the end of Chapter V, I have not discussed it.

Some of the material in the work has already appeared in the following journals: *Mind*, N.S. lxiii (1954); *The University of Toronto Quarterly*, xxiii (1954) and xxvi (1957); *Philosophy of Science*, xxii (1955); *The British Journal for the Philosophy of Science*, 9 (1958). I wish to thank the editors of those journals for their permission to use the relevant material. The editor of *Studia Varia, Royal Society of Canada Literary and Scientific Papers* (1957) has also granted me permission to use part of my essay, 'Progress and Evolution', which appeared in that volume.

University of Toronto   T. A. GOUDGE
May 15, 1960

CONTENTS

A philosophy which is to have any value should be built upon a wide and firm foundation of knowledge that is not specifically philosophical. Such knowledge is the soil from which the tree of philosophy derives its vigour. Philosophy which does not draw nourishment from this soil will soon wither and cease to grow.

BERTRAND RUSSELL

The Darwinian principle is plainly capable of great generalization. Wherever there are large numbers of objects having a tendency to retain certain characters unaltered, this tendency, however, not being absolute but giving room for chance variations, then, if the amount of variation is limited in certain directions by the destruction of everything which reaches those limits, there will be a gradual tendency to change in directions of departure from them. Thus if a million players sit down to bet at an even game, since one after another will get ruined, the average wealth of those who remain will perpetually increase. Here is indubitably a genuine formula of possible evolution. CHARLES PEIRCE

What has caused evolution? Why did it happen? What is its purpose, to what end is it directed? What is the meaning of evolution, and what is the meaning of that vastly greater world of which man is only a recent and minute fragment? Few of these questions are scientific . . . but it is important to recognize them for what they are, even if as scientists we must lay them aside. The biologist as philosopher cannot escape seeking answers to them, and neither can any thinking person.

G. G. SIMPSON
C. S. PITTENDRIGH
L. H. TIFFANY

CHAPTER I

INTRODUCTION

1. THE PURPOSE OF THE STUDY

A century has now elapsed since the period of intellectual ferment which followed the appearance of *The Origin of Species* (1859). This work not only revolutionized biological thought. It also profoundly affected the social sciences, the humanities, and even theology. The influence exerted by the work sprang from the unprecedented support it gave to the view that there had been an evolution of living things on the earth. Darwin's theory of evolution quickly became a powerful force in Western culture. Philosophy, like other disciplines, felt its impact. Thinkers such as Spencer, Peirce, Bergson and Dewey incorporated the theory in their systems. Throughout the whole range of this influence, however, it came to be assumed that the Darwinian doctrine was authoritative and to a large degree final. Even today, outside the field of biology, most people identify the theory of evolution with the ideas put forward by Darwin.

Meanwhile, within biology, the theory itself continued to evolve, so that what it means at present is different from what it meant a century ago. The most impressive changes have taken place quite recently. Thus, in 1951 it was said that the immediately preceding period 'proved to be the most fruitful decade in the history of evolutionary thought since the appearance of Darwin's classic in 1859' (Dobzhansky, 1951, ix).[1] Similarly, in 1953 it was remarked that 'the last ten years have produced a veritable revolution . . . in the breadth and nature of approach to evolutionary theory' (Simpson, 1953, ix). Many other authorities, such as Huxley (1942), Rensch (1947), Mayr (1942) and Carter (1951), have stressed the far-reaching nature of these developments.

[1] Bracketed references are to the work listed in the bibliography under the author's name and the date indicated. Where a quotation is given, the page reference is added.

This situation should excite the interest of philosophers who concern themselves with the results of the sciences. Not only does it provide an occasion for coming abreast of changes which have taken place in the theory of evolution, but it also offers fresh material for philosophical reflection. I have sought to take advantage of this situation in the present study. Its purpose is broadly twofold: first, to outline in a reasonably clear, non-technical way some major features of the new conception of evolution; and second, to investigate some philosophical questions which arise in connection with these features. There has been a tendency for philosophers to be over-impressed by the achievements of twentieth-century physics, and to neglect the achievements of twentieth-century biology. The following pages will show, I hope, that evolutionary theory gives rise to philosophical questions whose importance rivals anything physics has to offer.

The double purpose of the work requires the discussion to proceed on two levels. (i) Where the findings of evolutionary theory are outlined, and where conjectures are made on the basis of those findings, what is said belongs to the first-order level. The statements concerned are about living things, their history, and their probable future. Although I will discuss a good many biological details, I will try to avoid introducing technical *minutiae* which only specialists are competent to handle. I will likewise not presume to pass judgment on issues that remain controversial within evolutionary science, though notice will be taken of such issues from time to time. (ii) Where philosophical questions are considered, what is said belongs to the second-order level. The statements concerned are about various aspects of evolutionary theory, not about observable aspects of organisms. Hence this work contains no new information about the process or the causes of evolution. The providing of such information is exclusively a task for biologists. At various points the discussion shifts from one of the above levels to the other. But since the context nearly always makes plain on which level the discussion is proceeding, I have not thought it necessary to call attention to the shifts whenever they occur.

It will be well to give a short, preliminary account of the kinds of philosophical questions taken up in the study. They can be divided into three broad groups.

(A) There are, first of all, certain questions about the *language* used by biologists in expounding the theory of evolution. A number of their linguistic expressions have been taken over from ordinary speech (e.g. 'selection', 'adaptation', 'competition'), and are employed in special ways to convey scientific ideas. At first, these expressions have a predominantly figurative or metaphorical meaning in their specialized contexts. Repeated use, however, tends to alter the meaning so that the metaphorical aspects disappear. The expressions then become wholly technical terms whose significance is determined by their role in scientific discourse. Certain problems which this phenomenon generates will be discussed as we proceed. The phenomenon is prominent in a growing discipline such as evolutionary science is at present.

Another linguistic feature of a growing discipline is that its practitioners, in searching for ways of expressing new facts and of stating new conclusions, frequently mingle figurative and non-figurative forms of speech. This is a perfectly respectable procedure, since the notion that only literal language ought to be permitted in scientific discussions is antiquated. Plenty of things can be said effectively in science (and philosophy) by means of metaphors and analogies. What is important, of course, is not to confuse figurative expressions with those that are literal or technical. Otherwise, misconceptions easily arise. The history of popular Darwinism contains many examples of such misconceptions. By paying heed to the linguistic formulations of evolutionists, conceptual pitfalls created by the verbal expressions used can often be pointed out. Contrary to what some people think, this sort of philosophical activity is far from trivial. It is probable that the present study devotes too little, rather than too much, attention to the language of evolutionary theory.

(B) Another group of questions to be discussed is concerned with *logical* features of the theory of evolution. Here the theory is regarded as a 'framework' of concepts and statements. My aim will be to achieve some understanding of the inter-relations of certain of these concepts and statements within the framework.

Now it may be said that a *sine qua non* of understanding the logical features of a theory is to examine an axiomatic formulation of it. For only when we can discern its primitive concepts, postulates and theorems, together with the formation and transformation rules which govern them, can we make out how the theory is organized and achieve a proper degree of exactitude in its analysis. Hence the first step must surely be to find or construct an axiomatic version of evolutionary theory if questions about its logic are to be tackled.

No such step is taken in the present work, and the reasons for not taking it are the following. (i) The concepts which occur in a formalized axiomatic system have an absolutely fixed and precise meaning. In this respect they differ from concepts which refer to empirical facts. The latter concepts have an unavoidable imprecision, due to what has been called their 'open texture' (Waismann, 1945). The more complex the facts to which they refer, the greater will the imprecision be. Now the concepts which belong to evolutionary theory refer to facts whose complexity is enormous. Hence to treat these concepts as though they were absolutely precise, by incorporating them in a formal system, would be to distort them beyond recognition. (ii) The framework of statements constituting evolutionary theory is at present lacking in the tidiness and completeness which should exist before any axiomatization is undertaken. Since the theory is expounded discursively by biologists, it is often formulated in different ways with differences of emphasis on details. Modifications are being periodically introduced as fresh evidence comes to light and new theoretical interpretations are proposed. Any attempt to 'freeze' such a growing body of ideas in a formal scheme would result in grave misrepresentations. (iii) The theory of evolution contains as an essential part of its structure a number of historical statements. These deal with such phenomena as phylogenetic trends, adaptive radiation, the extinction of past forms of life, etc. But no evolutionist would be likely to agree that the statements of natural history can be deduced as logical consequences of a set of postulates. Consequently, the presence of historical statements makes its impossible to construct a full axiomatization of the theory. The issues involved in this third point are so important for the subsequent discussion that it will be advisable to set down a few further comments on them.

The theory of evolution, like any comprehensive scientific doctrine (e.g. modern atomic theory), has a powerful unifying function. It brings order into a large array of empirical evidence and helps to integrate the findings of numerous special disciplines. Like modern atomic theory it is abstract in character and requires for its formulation concepts which cannot be correlated with what is directly observable. In other respects, however, evolutionary theory is radically unlike comprehensive theories in physics and chemistry. For the latter are wholly systematic and non-historical, whereas the former combines systematic and historical elements. This 'double-barrelled' feature of evolutionary theory is one of its most distinctive characteristics. Part of the theory utilizes historical data in the form of fossils, reconstructs unique, non-recurrent evolutionary histories, and advances historical explanations. Another part of the theory utilizes non-historical data derived from observation of contemporary organisms, incorporates many of the generalizations of such special sciences as genetics, ecology, embryology, comparative anatomy, etc, and makes use of law-like statements in formulating systematic explanations. The logical relations within each of these parts and between them are by no means easy to disentangle. But at least it seems clear that no axiomatic approach to the matter is appropriate. In trying to understand the structure of evolutionary theory, the best we can do is to proceed discursively, aiming at as much exactness of statement as the condition of biological knowledge warrants but being careful not to give the theory a spurious precision and tidiness.

Closely connected with the above are certain questions which concern the use of 'theoretical models' in interpreting evolutionary phenomena. These models are of various kinds, extending all the way from simple, pictorial devices, such as Darwin's 'tree of life', to abstract topographical and statistical patterns. Although their function is partly heuristic, it is not exclusively so. Often the formulation of some aspect of evolutionary theory derives its meaning from a model associated with it. There is an intrinsic connection between theory and model here, as elsewhere in science. Yet every scientific model depends on the presence of analogies, and involves a radical simplification or 'idealization' of what exists in nature. Hence, unless it is employed with caution, its effects may be misleading. Special dangers attach to the use of pictorial models in thinking about the history of life (Cf. Umbgrove, 1950). And in general, 'the price of the employment of models is eternal vigilance' (Braithwaite, 1953, 93). This admonition will be remembered as we take note of various evolutionary models that have been devised.

(C) The final group of questions to be considered below I have called 'metaphysical'. Without giving a detailed account of them

B

at this stage, I will simply remark that some of them arise when the conclusions of evolutionary theory are interpreted as being about a single, historical process having an existential status of its own, quite apart from any theories concerning it. This interpretation is not a scientifically verifiable contention. It does not belong to the framework of statements constituting evolutionary theory. But it may, nevertheless, be a 'metaphysical implication' of that theory. Furthermore, the questions which arise in connection with the interpretation are not amenable to scientific answers. Yet despite this, they do not appear to lack intelligibility or to be incapable of analysis. These matters are treated at greater length in Chapter V. I may add that the questions, not their designation, are what interest me. So if anyone objects to my use of 'metaphysical', I am quite prepared to substitute some other adjective (e.g. 'metabiological') for it.

The purpose of the present study is, then, to review major aspects of the ascent of life as depicted by modern evolutionary theory, and to examine a number of linguistic, logical, and metaphysical questions which can be asked in the light of that theory. I do not profess to give final answers to any of these questions. But I do profess to show that the questions are important and worthy of more attention than they have recently received. Since the ideas of Darwin have been so profoundly influential in determining opinions on this subject, I will devote some space at the start to an outline of his doctrine. This will put us in an advantageous position to see the extent of the change which has occurred in the theory of evolution since his day.

2. THE DARWINIAN VERSION OF EVOLUTION

By the time *The Origin of Species* appeared, most scientific men had come to accept a number of conclusions about the plants and animals inhabiting the earth. Geological evidence concerning the temporal order of rock strata, together with the evidence of fossil remains of organisms in those strata, made it fairly certain that there had been a succession of living things on the earth for an immensely long period of time. Hence, it was concluded, all organisms now living have descended from other organisms, usually very different in character, which lived in the remote past. Furthermore, the record showed that many of the differences between ancient and modern forms of life had arisen gradually through the ages, so that if all the individuals which had ever existed could be assembled a broadly continuous array of forms would be found. Thus, the old, fixed lines of demarcation among types of organisms were becoming blurred in the face of the evidence that living things had in the course of time changed their form and function as a result of a gradual, continuous process. To determine the details of that process, and so to compile a complete natural history, was considered by most biologists before 1859 to be their central task.

Darwin was one of the few people to see the importance of the causal as well as the historical aspect of evolution. While the two aspects are not always carefully distinguished in his writing, he did think that his prime objective was to formulate a scientifically acceptable account of the factors which had produced the changes disclosed by natural history. We may follow Huxley (1942) in summarizing the essential features of Darwin's account.

It is a fact that organisms tend to produce offspring which, in the earliest stages of their existence, are more numerous than their parents. 'Excessive reproduction' is the rule throughout living nature. Consequently, every type of organism tends to increase its numbers at a rate approximating a geometric progression. Yet it is also a fact that the numbers of a given type of organism remain very nearly constant through long stretches of time, and even when the numbers are increasing, the rate at which they do so falls far short of any geometric progression. From these two facts Darwin inferred that among the young of every type of organism competition for survival must occur, as a result of which many offspring die before reaching maturity. Among those who do mature, there is a further competition in reproductive activity. To designate both varieties of competition, Darwin used the expression 'struggle for existence'. He declared that this expression was not to be taken literally, but was to be understood in 'a large and metaphorical sense'. However, he did not always use it metaphorically; and many of his followers, including T. H. Huxley, regarded the struggle for existence as literally pervading the whole of organic nature.

The third fact utilized by Darwin was the occurrence of numerous variations in the characters possessed by the members of each species. From this fact, together with the doctrine of the struggle for existence, he made a further inference, namely, that variations which assist individuals to survive and reproduce will be preserved in the species, while variations unfavourable to survival and reproduction will gradually be eliminated. To this process he gave the name 'natural selection'—another metaphor, incidentally, but one which was often construed both by himself and his followers in a literal sense. Since many variations are undoubtedly transmitted from parents to offspring, natural selection will produce, he contended, a slow accumulation of favourable variations in a species from generation to generation. Accordingly, a species possessing such variations will become better and better adapted to a fixed way of life, or will shift from one way of life to another, while species lacking the variations in question will slowly disappear. Furthermore, members of the surviving species will gradually change their observable form and functions in successive generations, so that ultimately a new species will be produced. Natural selection is, therefore, the main cause of the origin of species and of the historical course taken by living things.

One important feature of this causal account of evolution is that it was profoundly affected by Darwin's reading of Malthus' *An Essay on the Principles of Population*, from which, in October 1838, he derived the initial stimulus for his theory. Hence *The Origin of Species* reflects the influence of Malthusian ideas and terminology, not always to its advantage. Thus one of the 'facts' which Darwin's account utilized, namely, that all living things reproduce at a geometric rate, is not an empirical generalization, but rather an extension of Malthus' doctrine of 'excessive reproduction'. This doctrine, we will discover, is now regarded as erroneous. Malthus' expression 'struggle for existence' was scarcely a desirable one for Darwin to adopt. It gave rise to needless misinterpretations, some of which we will consider below. Darwin himself was fully conscious of the influence at work here. He even describes the theory of natural selection as 'the doctrine of Malthus applied with manifold force to the whole animal and vegetable kingdoms'.

Quite apart from this, Darwin's formulation of the doctrine of natural selection exposed it to adverse criticisms. Thus it was said that selection could at best explain the *elimination* of certain types of organisms, since all it did was to show how, given individual organisms with a great range of variations, those possessing unfavourable variations died out leaving the remainder unaffected. Natural selection is therefore wholly destructive or eliminative, not creative. It cannot account even for the preservation, let alone the production, of species. To be sure, the process does throw light on the problem of the geographical distribution of organisms, and offers a plausible explanation of why some species have died out in one place and other species in another. But this is quite different from explaining how new species have come into being. On the latter problem, natural selection throws no light at all.

Another criticism was that as a process inferred rather than observed to occur, natural selection was not based on a solid foundation. This criticism was often put forward by those who were interested in making biology a precise, quantitative science. To them Darwin's discussion of biological issues was far too inexact and speculative to be satisfactory. Thus, from the observed fact that a characteristic possessed by an organism appears to be useful to that organism, Darwin deduced that the characteristic is an adaptation due to natural selection operating in the course of the evolutionary process. But such a deduction is couched in qualitative terms which are extremely vague. It is not based on any experimental work showing the concrete biological value of the adaptation. It cannot be checked by reference to exact observations, demonstrating how natural selection functions in nature. When at the turn of the century the young science of genetics was advancing rapidly as a result of its experimental data, geneticists often levelled this criticism against Darwinism.

There can be no doubt that the major limitation in Darwin's theory was due to his lack of knowledge concerning the factors and laws of heredity. This lack, which he shared with his contemporaries, is apparent in his view of the variations on which natural selection operates. Thus he believed that some variations due to the direct action of the environment on the individual organism were transmitted from parents to offspring; and that other variations due to the individual's use or disuse of different organs or functions were similarly transmitted. The great bulk of variations, however, he held to be those which arose quite spontaneously. While they presumably have causes, we remain in the dark as to what these causes are or how they operate. Such variations are 'random' in the sense that they are not correlated with the particular adaptive needs of the individual organisms in which they arise. Moreover, Darwin thought, such random variations occur 'in every direction' in each generation of a species. All the variations utilized by natural selection are of a minute kind. If favourable, they are piled up through a continuous process of accumulation; and if unfavourable, they are slowly eliminated. Some cause must be supposed constantly at work retaining inherited variations within a species, although we cannot say how it performs this function.

It has been pointed out by Fisher (1930) and others that Darwin subscribed to the so-called 'blending theory of inheritance' prevalent in his day. This theory assumed that whatever physical agency determined inherited characters, the latter blended with one another in the process of reproduction, like equal quantities of differently coloured ink. Once the characters had become 'mixed' they could never function again in their original form. A consequence of this theory was that the variability present in a species must rapidly diminish in a few generations. With random mating it would diminish by approximately 50 per cent. in each generation. Since this consequence was at odds with what was actually observed in nature, Darwin had to assume (a) that environmental conditions can cause large-scale outbursts of variations, and (b) that in the case of each existing species such an outburst had taken place in the very recent past. Unless both assumptions were made, a species which had existed for a considerable length of time would exhibit almost no variations at all. Natural selection would then be unable to function and evolution would come to a stop. Yet it was fairly plain that these assumptions, like the blending theory of inheritance itself, left much to be desired. Until they were improved, or replaced by something better, the problem of evolutionary causality could not be satisfactorily tackled.

The title Darwin chose for his major work is indicative of other limitations in his doctrine. Since the work is mainly devoted to discussing the process of evolutionary change and the factors which have brought it about, the title suggests that evolution is synonymous with the origin of species. This seems to have been in fact Darwin's view. But, as we now know, evolution may go on even though no new species are being produced; and conversely, an extensive multiplication of species is compatible with rather minor evolutionary changes. The title further suggests that the work offers an account of the manner in which species originate. But the very concept of a species was vaguely defined in Darwin's day, and he himself recognized no essential difference between species and varieties. Finally, Darwin did not stress sufficiently the rôle played by reproductive isolation in generating and maintaining evolutionary diversity among different kinds of organisms. These facts, together with the lack of knowledge of how hereditary variations arise, made an adequate theory of the origin of species impossible in 1859.

The above criticisms and limitations were not serious enough to prevent Darwin's doctrine from being espoused by the majority of biologists in his day. Even conservative minds considered it a sound working hypothesis, far more satisfactory than any competing doctrine. Moreover, there seemed to be no reason why, with the increase of biological knowledge, the doctrine could not be formulated more precisely. Such a reformulation has in fact been largely achieved during the past few decades, when the reaction against Darwinism has been replaced by a synthesis of Darwinian concepts with the major conclusions of genetics. Some features of this synthesis will shortly occupy us.

One consequence of Darwin's work, which excited great general interest, was that it made no use of teleological notions in its account of how living things had developed on the earth. Thus the external teleology implied by the Biblical doctrine of a special creation of species was shown to be scientifically superfluous. Darwin himself believed when he wrote The Origin of Species that evolution had begun with one, or any rate a very few forms, into which life had been 'breathed by the Creator'. From these primary organisms, in accordance with the principle of natural selection, all the subsequent diversity of species had been produced. Hence, the course of evolution depicted by The Origin of Species could not be held to exemplify, either in its detailed or its over-all character, any transcendent purpose. What took place was due to the operation of natural, not supernatural, factors. External teleology was thus excluded from biological theory. It was often said that this consequence makes the course of evolution 'blind and pointless', or wholly 'random', and hence lacking a direction or goal.

The Darwinian doctrine also appeared to render superfluous any appeal to internal teleology. Prior to Darwin, it had seemed reasonable to point to the manifold and often elaborate adaptations of organisms to their environment as evidence of the operation of a teleological agency within those organisms. On the Darwinian hypothesis, however, natural selection was proposed as an adequate explanation of all such phenomena. No reference to inner purposes, conscious or unconscious, was needed. The most that could be admitted was the *appearance* of teleology.

As is well known, this repudiation of teleological notions was attacked by those who espoused theistic or spiritualistic views of the cosmos. Yet towards the close of the century, a thinly disguised form of teleology began to reappear, chiefly among workers in paleontology. Many of them found it impossible to reconcile the alleged randomness of the evolutionary process with the fact of orderly changes disclosed by the fossil record. In numerous cases there were series of fossils which showed that the organisms concerned had undergone a systematic transformation for long periods of time. Looking at each series as a whole, it was contended that one could detect a definite trend which was maintained even in the face of a changing environment. All this seemed incompatible with Darwinism. Consequently, many paleontologists at the beginning of the twentieth century were sympathetic to some form of 'orthogenesis', that is, to the view that evolutionary changes were due to an inner 'perfecting principle' which determined the general direction of change in at least a number of cases. This view involved a soft-pedalling, or an outright rejection, of natural selection, and gave rise to the belief that 'Darwinism is dead'. Confident pronouncements to this effect were often made from the pulpits of the time.

How matters stand at present with regard to the above issues will be indicated as we proceed. It is clear, however, that the general interpretation of evolution accepted today differs from that of Darwin in many respects. His version of natural selection is held to contain only part of the truth. His view of species and their formation represents only the start of an acceptable theory. His conception of variations and their transmission has been scrapped. Nevertheless it is because of his monumental achievement that subsequent advances have been possible. The significance of the developments to which we will now turn can only be understood in the light of what he accomplished.

CHAPTER II

HISTORICAL ASPECTS OF EVOLUTION

1. EVOLUTION AND CHANGE

Whatever else may be signified by the word 'evolution', it undoubtedly refers to a type of *change* which has taken and is taking place in the world. This can be seen by a moment's reflection on the ordinary, non-technical use of the word. It would sound self-contradictory to say: 'The automobile evolved from the horseless carriage, but no changes of any kind occurred.' Whenever we are prepared to use the word 'evolution' we are also prepared to use the word 'change'. Similarly, it would sound queer to say: 'The number of sides of a Euclidean triangle has evolved.' Since the word 'change' is not used in connection with the properties of triangles, the word 'evolution' cannot be used either. Where there is no possibility of change there can be no evolution. But many occasions arise on which we speak about change and yet would not speak about evolution. Thus we say, 'Water cooled to 0° C. changes into ice,' but not 'Water cooled to 0° C. evolves into ice'; 'Blue litmus placed in acid turns red,' but not: 'Blue litmus placed in acid evolves into red litmus.' Clearly, then, while evolution is a type of change, 'evolution' and 'change' are not synonymous terms.

Reflection on ordinary usage will take us a little further than this. It is proper to describe a river-delta or a crystal in a supersaturated solution as increasing in size, but not as 'evolving' in size. We can even speak of the river-delta or the crystal 'growing', much as we say that an acorn grows to be an oak or a child grows to be an adult. But we would not say that an acorn 'evolves' into an oak or that a child 'evolves' into an adult. Ordinary usage thus suggests that evolution is different from both quantitative increase and growth. Two centuries ago, indeed, it was accepted practice to apply the term 'evolution' to the process of 'unfolding' by which an individual organism arises from a seed or an egg. Today the term 'development' is reserved for this ontogenetic process. Thus the germination of a seed and changes which occur in a fertilized ovum are described as developmental but not as evolutionary processes. Even at the level of non-technical speech, therefore, it appears that evolution is a type of change different from mere quantitative increase, individual growth, and individual development.

Now there are three important general questions which can be asked about any sort of change: *What is it that changes? How does it change?* and *What causes it to change?* In the present chapter we will be concerned with the first and second of these questions, as applied to evolution. That is to say, we will undertake to outline and comment on the answers proposed by contemporary biologists to the questions: *What is it that evolves?* and *How does it evolve?* These queries have to do primarily with the historical aspects of evolutionary theory.

2. POPULATIONS AS THE UNITS OF EVOLUTION

Until quite recently it would have been considered satisfactory to say that 'living things', 'organisms', or 'species' are what evolve. Nowadays the tendency is to avoid this way of speaking, on the ground that a more empirical approach is desirable. Empirically, what a laboratory or field biologist studies are groups of plants or animals living together in a certain region of space for a certain period of time. These groups are referred to as 'populations'. This expression, taken over from the vocabulary of statistics, has come to assume a central place in evolutionary theory on both its historical and systematic sides. For at the most elementary level, it is said, populations are the *units* which undergo evolution. They, rather than 'living things' or 'species', are what evolve (Cf. Simpson, 1944; Mayr, 1949b; Carter, 1951). Our first step, therefore, must be to examine the concept of a population and see what it involves.

In current biological usage, the term 'population' refers to a group of individual organisms standing in certain relations to each other. Unless some organisms having these relations to each other are involved, it is not appropriate to speak of a population at all. The term is accordingly not applicable to every collection of plants or animals. We may say, then, that the ultimate units of a population are individuals. No general definition of 'biological individuality' is presupposed by this statement.

All it means is that certain discrete items or 'members' of a population can be distinguished. Hence the population can be treated quantitatively. Biologists can determine such statistical features as its birth-rate, death-rate, etc., and can represent it by an over-all census figure. Whether there is any warrant for considering a population to be a kind of 'supraorganism', as has sometimes been done, is a question we may put aside for the moment.

Must the individual organisms which constitute a population be actually living? W. C. Allee and his associates (1949) state that 'aliveness' is one of the concepts needed to give a formal definition of a population. That this is doubtful may be seen by distinguishing three cases. (i) A population may be, and usually is, regarded as enduring in time, so that while it continues some of its constituent individuals die and others are born. Hence in speaking of the population we include both the actually living members and their deceased ancestors. (ii) We can by abstraction limit our consideration to the present constitution of the population and so include only the members of it which are alive. Here we consider a momentary cross-section of a larger temporal whole. The features thus revealed will be quite different from case (i), and may be of interest to anyone studying what has been called 'the statics of evolution' (Haldane, 1954b). (iii) The use of the concept of a population by paleontologists in reaching conclusions about extinct organisms constitutes a third case. Here none of the constituent organisms are alive, although we infer that they were alive at some time in the past. It is clear, then, that 'aliveness' is not essential to the notion of a population except in case (ii).

Because it involves a reference to space and time, the concept of a population has a degree of vagueness about it which is inescapable. In the vast majority of instances, the exact temporal duration of a population cannot be determined; and as far as natural populations go, it may not even make sense to ask precisely when any one of them began or ended. Certainly, the temporal categories of paleontology cover millions of years, and it is usually impossible to do more than locate a group of organisms in the particular period or epoch in which it arose or disappeared. Even the apparent temporal precision of case (ii) depends upon leaving unspecified what is meant by a 'momentary cross-section' of a population.

But it is the spatial aspect of populations which gives rise to the greatest vagueness. In order to see why this is so we must note that the chief relations which individual organisms need to have if they are to form a population arise from the reproductive process. For the sake of simplicity, we may limit our attention to animals whose mode of reproduction is biparental. Here it is obvious that the reproductive process establishes among the animals mating, progeny, and parenthood relations. The process also makes possible the transmission of hereditary factors (genes and chromosomes) from one generation to the next. Since the transmission proceeds in accordance with genetic laws, the organisms are often said to form a 'Mendelian population'.

Reproduction or interbreeding is thus a major integrating agency in all such groups. But if animals are to interbreed they must be near one another. Spatial proximity is necessary for the occurrence of the reproductive process. The animals must inhabit the same geographical region and so are a 'local population'. Being in spatial proximity, the members of a local population will interbreed most frequently with one another, and thus be a fairly self-contained or isolated collection. Such collections are now held to be of basic importance in evolution. Thus it is sometimes said that what evolves is a local population *in toto*, not any smaller group making up a part of it (Carter, 1951).

A moment's reflection will show that no exact spatial delimitation can be expected here. We cannot say precisely where the boundaries of a local population are because it has no precise boundaries. Take what seems *prima facie* to be the simplest case, *viz.* a group of interbreeding land animals on an island which is completely isolated yet small enough to allow any one animal to range over the whole of its surface. We can say that the spatial extent of this local population will never be larger than the geographical area of the island, and is almost sure to be smaller. But we can scarcely achieve greater accuracy than that. Various proposals have been put forward to make possible the delimiting of a population of bisexual animals with more definiteness. For example, we might take a particular pair (male and female) as a centre, and regard the population as all those animals with which each of the pair can interbreed. Since interbreeding is most likely to occur in the immediate neighbourhood of the pair, there will be a steady decrease in the likelihood of interbreeding as the distance from the pair increases. Except in special cases like that of the island population, however, no point can be fixed at which the likelihood of interbreeding disappears. Moreover, as the two central animals travel about their region, the population they define continually shifts its geographical locus. Other changes may also take place, such as the adding of new animals by birth and immigration, and the loss of old animals by death and emigration. It seems clear, then, that the spatial as well as the temporal boundaries of a population are unavoidably vague (Cf. Burma, 1949).

In considering the rôle of the concept of a population in evolutionary theory, certain further distinctions seem to be required (Cf. Simpson, 1953).

(A) A plant or animal population can be considered as all those individuals in a given region of space which are potentially inter-fertile. Not only those which do actually interbreed, but those which are capable of interbreeding, compose the population. It is therefore representable by a census figure which would result from counting its constituent individuals. Either a temporal cross-section or a long temporal span of the population can be represented by such a figure. Ideally, the figure is a perfectly determinate one, and it can, perhaps, be arrived at in the case of small well-demarcated groups (e.g. in a laboratory cage, etc.). But in the case of the great majority of wild populations, the figure is bound to be approximate if it is arrived at on empirical grounds. The criterion which determines whether a particular individual is to be counted in the census is its ability to inter-breed with other members of the group.

(B) It nearly always happens that some members of (A) fail to leave offspring, usually because they do not reach maturity. These members may affect the group's evolution in a variety of ways, but they do not contribute hereditary factors to subse-quent generations. Hence it has proved necessary to discriminate within (A) all those individuals which actually interbreed. They form what is called 'the effective breeding population' (Simpson, 1953, 116). This group is the vehicle by which genetic material is transmitted from one generation to the next. The census figure of the effective breeding population will always be slightly or markedly smaller than that of (A). Groups of this type have been extensively investigated in recent years by students of population genetics. As we will see, their work has led to the construction of statistical models which have thrown fresh light on the evolutionary process.

(C) One of the standard conditions specified in these models is that breeding populations shall be regarded as panmictic. Their individual constituents are assumed to be subject to random inter-breeding. This condition facilitates the application of statistical techniques, and provides a basis for exploring systematically different deviations from the norm. But most effective breeding populations in nature are not panmictic because they contain localized sub-groups which have some degree of isolation from one another. Within each of these sub-groups, however, random interbreeding does occur. Consequently, they have been distinguished from groups of type (B) and have been called 'demes' (Cf. Gilmour and Gregor, 1939; Huxley, 1942; Carter, 1951). A deme is literally a community of interbreeding organisms, 'the smallest collective unit' of an animal population (Simpson, 1953, 380).

Some students prefer to regard demes as local populations in the strictest sense. Others affirm that demes are parts of a local population construed in a sense which makes it identical with (A) above. The latter usage permits us to say that local populations are at bottom what evolve, whereas the former usage would not permit us to say this, at least according to Simpson. For he states: 'Demes are not by nature units that are evolving into sub-species . . . These units are still in a genetic continuum, and a subspecies normally arises by limited exchange of genetic factors among demes so that a number of them come to have a distinctive facies, generally adaptive in nature, sufficiently defined and lasting for useful taxonomic recognition' (Simpson, 1953, 380). The usual situation is that demes in a sub-divided population intergrade with one another and hence differ so little that there is no point in recognizing them as taxonomically distinct. It is not implied, of course, that a deme is completely homogeneous or lacking in internal differentiation.

The chief attributes of populations fall into two classes. In the first class occur a number of quantitative or statistical attributes. Among these are: (i) birth rate and death rate; (ii) dispersion or numerical distribution of the population in space and time; (iii) density or the number of individuals in the population per unit of space they occupy; and (iv) the systematic changes which take place in the size of the population during its history. This last feature has proved amenable to study by means of graphs, and when so treated has been called the 'growth form' of the population (Allee, 1949, 263-65). Certain well-marked phases of the growth form, such as the phase of positive growth, of equilibrium, oscillation, decline and extinction, have been designated. All the attributes in this class belong to the population as a *whole* or, more precisely, an 'open system', composed of individual organisms (Cf. Mainx, 1954; Bertalanffy, 1950, 1952). The attributes therefore characterize the population uniquely, but do not characterize its members. In other words, we have here a group of system-attributes expressible as statistical functions.

The second class of attributes which have been discriminated are non-quantitative. According to some authors, these attributes are such that they characterize both a population and its individual constituents. They have been enumerated as follows: '(i) The population has a definite structure and composition which is constant for any moment of time but fluctuates with age. (ii) The population is ontogenetic. It exhibits (as does the organism) growth, differentiation and division of labour, maintenance, senescence, and death. (iii) The population has a heredity. (iv) The population is integrated by both genetic and ecologic factors that operate as interdependent mechanisms. (v) Like the organism, the population is a unit that meets the impact of the environment. This is a reciprocal phenomenon, since the population is altered as a consequence of this impact, and, in time, it alters its effective environment' (Allee, 1949, 264).

The underlying point of view here is one which takes a population to be not merely an open system or whole, but a kind of supraorganism, sharing with its individual constituents certain organismic attributes. For some purposes it may be useful to regard a population in this way, but there are dangers in trying to press the analogy between an individual organism and a population too far. For the analogy is in fact superficial, and if it is mistaken for more than that, both linguistic and conceptual confusion will be generated.

Consider, for example, the ontogenetic attribute of senescence. The majority of individual organisms go through a process of aging and eventually die. A few biologists have contended that populations or 'races' are subject to the same process (Cf. Schindewolf, 1936; Vandel, 1949). This contention has often been put forward as part of a theory of cyclic evolution according to which each population has a juvenile, adult and senile phase, in that order. There is considerable doubt, however, as to the propriety of this way of speaking, since according to various students no analogy exists between a population and an organism with regard to senescence. Thus Simpson has declared that 'the term "senility" applied to evolving groups is a misused metaphor where not even analogy exists. Nothing in a continuously reproducing population does or can possibly correspond with the process of aging in an individual' (Simpson, 1953, 291). The ontogenetic phases of the individual are known to be defined and conditioned by factors that have no analogues in the factors which condition the ancestral and descendant sequences of populations.

Similar considerations are relevant to the contention that both individual organisms and populations have a 'structure'. If this term is understood in a general sense to refer to the fact that in both cases we can distinguish a set of parts having a certain spatial arrangement and certain modes of functional correlation with each other, then the contention is no doubt defensible. But such a general approach fails to take account of the important respects in which the two cases differ. Thus, for example, the parts (cells, tissues, organs, etc.) which enter into the structure of a multicellular plant or animal are so intimately co-ordinated that as a rule they are in direct organic continuity with one another. But the structure of a population is not usually characterized by the organic continuity of its parts (the individuals which compose it). Furthermore, the functioning of the parts of a plant or animal structure is directed toward maintaining a state of relative equilibrium within the organism as a whole or between the organism and its environment. The behaviour of individuals in a population, however, is not ordinarily directed towards preserving its equilibrium. The particular state of a population at a particular time is rather a statistical consequence of the behaviour of its parts. In other words, populations and organisms are quite different kinds of systems with different kinds of structure. To speak of them 'sharing a common attribute' here is to obscure what should be kept clear.

How are we to understand the contention that a population, like an individual, has a heredity? Suppose we consider a population as specified in case (ii) above, i.e. as a momentary cross-section of a larger, spatio-temporal (though vaguely delimited) whole. We can hardly say that such a population has a heredity in the sense in which this can be affirmed of its individual constituents. For each of the units which makes up an individual's hereditary equipment is located in every cell of his body. But each of the genetic units in a population is not present in every one of its members. Moreover, there are now good grounds for thinking that an individual's hereditary equipment is not merely the sum of certain units, but is rather an integrated system formed by the interaction of these units. The population's 'heredity' on the other hand does not normally appear to be such an integrated system. Geneticists sometimes speak of a 'gene pool' in which the members of a Mendelian population 'share' (Dobzhansky, 1951). This suggests the idea of a common fund of independent units. At other times, reference is made to the 'corporate genotype' of a population. Yet according to Dobzhansky this expression merely designates 'a function of the genetic constitution of the component individuals, just as the health of an individual body is a function of the soundness of its parts. The rules governing the genetic structure of a population are, nevertheless, distinct from those which govern the genetics of individuals, just as the rules of sociology are distinct from physiological ones, although the former are in the last analysis integrated systems of the latter (Dobzhansky, 1951, 15).

The result of this part of the discussion may be summarized as follows. In current usage the term 'population' applies to any collection of individual organisms which is such that it persists or did persist through a finite though vaguely delimited span of time in a vaguely delimited region of space on the earth's surface; its ultimate constituents are organisms which are or were alive; it is a type of open system which interacts with the environment and is analysable into various sub-systems such as demes, which are partially isolated from one another, of transitory duration, and subject to inter-grading; its constituent organisms in any temporal cross-section must be potentially inter-fertile, and in any temporal stretch which includes more than one generation of the population, the organisms must be linked by actual mating, progeny and parenthood relations so that there

C

is a transmission of hereditary material from earlier to later members; it is characterized by various attributes, some statistical and some qualitative; its members must be capable of living together in relative or total isolation from other populations.

Further, since a population is an open system, we may speak of it as an 'entity' or 'whole', provided we do not allow ourselves to think that we are referring to something which has an independent status apart from individual organisms and their interrelationships. But it is improper, or at least gravely misleading, to speak of a population as a kind of supraorganism, sharing certain ontogenetic attributes with its constituents.

Finally, we have said that populations are the ultimate units of evolution, since they are basically what evolve. This means that it is inadmissible to use the term 'evolution' (a) when referring to changes which take place in the constituents of populations, i.e. to the development, growth, degeneration, etc., of individual organisms; and (b) unless some change has gone on or is going on in some population. There is no need, however, to ban all talk about the evolution of living things, organisms, or species. This is often a convenient way of speaking, and carries no implication that the phenomena referred to involve something different from changes in populations.

3. THE HISTORY OF POPULATIONS AS A RECONSTRUCTION

The whole evolutionary process can be viewed as the history of all the populations which have existed on earth. In order to make out the details of so multifarious a phenomenon, biologists have to assemble as much empirical evidence as they can and interpret it in the light of various hypotheses and assumptions. In this respect the task of tracing the history of populations is no different in principle from any other inquiry into past occurrences. Such occurrences are not directly accessible. They can only be got at through the records or traces of them which have survived and are utilizable by those conducting the inquiry. Moreover, hypotheses and assumptions have to be introduced; and the more fragmentary the records or traces, the more elaborate must the scheme of hypotheses and assumptions be. Accordingly, the account which is given of the history of living things has to be recognized as a set of conclusions derived from interpretations of the available evidence. The account cannot be an 'eye-witness report' but must be a theoretical reconstruction of what took place. It will therefore be appropriate to mention the major items which enter into this reconstruction and to arrange them in a roughly logical sequence.

(A) The most fundamental item consists of the extensive body of evidence formed by objects which have been observed in various strata of rocks near the earth's surface. These objects are now universally assumed to be fossils, i.e. the remains and traces of animals and plants which lived in the past. Without this assumption, which is clearly an interpretation of what is directly observed, the scientific theory of evolution could not be formulated.

(B) To determine the age and temporal order of fossil remains, it is necessary to assume the correctness of certain geological conclusions about the age and order of superposition of the strata in which the remains are embedded. While geologists do sometimes appeal to the evidence of fossil sequences in establishing these conclusions, there are cases where the order of superposition and succession of strata can be fixed independently of such evidence. In any case, the determination of that order is the responsibility of the geologist, and the biologist simply accepts the geological conclusions without question.

(C) The known fossils permit of being classified so that they exemplify a number of distinct types of organisms. The fossils can also, in virtue of (B), be arranged serially from the earliest to the most recent. When this is done, it becomes apparent that there are many gaps, both large and small, in the record. The empirical evidence is therefore fragmentary or wholly lacking at various points.
Several different assumptions can be made with regard to these gaps. (i) It may be held that they are due to the fact that the relevant fossils have not yet been discovered. (ii) It may be held that while some missing fossils are undiscovered, others are missing because they do not exist. Their non-existence constitutes a permanent gap in the record. Nevertheless, during the time-span corresponding to the gap organisms existed which did not become fossilized, and hence we do not need to suppose that there was

any gap in the succession of living things. Indeed, the vast majority of plants and animals have left no remains behind them because the conditions required for fossilization are of relatively rare occurrence. (iii) It may be held that while some of the missing fossils are merely undiscovered, many gaps in the record exist because no organisms of the appropriate type existed to become fossilized. The gaps therefore represent actual discontinuities in the history of living things. The evolutionary process cannot therefore be regarded as always and everywhere continuous. It may be doubted whether anyone today would defend position (i). But with respect to (ii) and (iii) a legitimate controversy has developed among biologists. We will take note of it at a subsequent stage of our discussion.

(D) All the organisms we can observe arise from other organisms as a result of reproduction. It is assumed that this has always been true, at least as far back in time as the fossil evidence extends. The members of each generation are therefore held to be the offspring of members belonging to the immediately preceding generation. Hence, speaking metaphorically, we may say that reproduction is the link which connects the individual members of successive generations in an unbroken series. It is well to keep in mind that this is a metaphorical way of speaking, for otherwise we may be tempted to talk about the 'continuity' of all living things, or about the 'biological continuum', as though these expressions were to be interpreted literally. But, of course, in the vast majority of cases a fully developed organism is not even 'continuous' with its parents, let alone its remote ancestors. The more closely our use of the notion of continuity approximates to the mathematical meaning of the term, the less appropriately does it apply to the process of descent. The conclusion that *omne vivum e vivo* underlines quite a different point, namely that the occurrence of reproduction is essential to evolution. In other words, the evolutionary process is *biogenetic*.

It is natural at this point to ask whether there is not an exception to the conclusion just stated. The very *first* living things cannot have arisen as a result of biotic reproduction, since only non-living things preceded them and these are incapable of exemplifying any reproductive functions. Accordingly, if the evolutionary standpoint is to be sustained, must we not say that the first organisms evolved from inorganic substances in a way which did not require biotic reproduction? But if so, the latter process is not essential to evolution. In that case, can we rule out the possibility that at numerous points in the past new types of living things (e.g. micro-organisms) may have arisen in a similar manner from the non-living world? If this occurrence took place once, why may it not have taken place many times?

Several different replies can be made to these questions. It may be said, for example, that we do not need to suppose that there ever *were* any beings to whom the designation 'the first living things' could be applied. For, as Haldane has pointed out, it is quite possible that living and non-living things are co-eternal in the universe. On such an hypothesis 'matter and life have always existed. When stars become habitable, they are colonized by "seeds" of life from interstellar space, perhaps spores of bacteria or simple plants' (Haldane, 1954a, 12). This view does not clash with any available scientific evidence, and may turn out to be the only tenable position if alternative hypotheses prove unsatisfactory. It is therefore by no means settled that there *has* been an 'evolution' of the organic from the inorganic. In the absence of conclusive grounds for supposing that the first living things on the earth were also the first living things, we are not obliged to admit any exception to the principle that terrestrial evolution requires the presence of biotic reproduction.

If it be objected that the odds strongly favour the conclusion that the first living things on the earth arose from inorganic substances, another reply may be made. The emergence of the living from the non-living, it may be said, can hardly have been in the strict sense a process of biological evolution such as took place after the first organisms appeared. At best, this emergence must have involved a kind of 'biochemical evolution' the features of which were so different from what happened subsequently that it is doubtful whether the term 'evolution' ought to be applied to it at all (Bernal, 1951). In any case, the theory of biological evolution is limited to what occurred between the point in time at which the earliest living things existed and the present. For the theory on its historical side does not go beyond the assertion that existing organisms are descended from organisms which existed in the remote past. And the sequence of events making up this descent is undoubtedly biogenetic, i.e. it depends on the occurrence of reproductive functions. Without reproduction there can be no evolution as we know it.

The above are major items in the historical reconstruction of how populations have evolved. It will be observed that each of the items embodies certain observed facts and certain assumptions. In the light of the facts and assumptions a number of conclusions have been reached about large-scale features of the evolutionary process. Our next task will be to review the most significant of these features.

4. LARGE-SCALE FEATURES OF EVOLUTION

The history of living things on the earth has been spoken of as a single process. When one speaks thus within the context of biology, one is talking at a high level of abstractness. The justification for so speaking is derived from other statements belonging to the framework of evolutionary theory, e.g. the statement that life began at a certain time in its terrestrial setting, that its history has taken place in a finite region of space, that successive generations of organisms are related reproductively so as to form an unbroken series in accordance with the biogenetic principle, and that throughout their history the organisms concerned have undergone changes in practically all their characteristics. These statements provide a basis on which scientific meaning can be given to the contention that there is a single process of evolution. An indirect connection between the contention and what is observable in nature can be set up within evolutionary theory.

Now the features manifested by this single process are divisible into (i) those which characterize it as a whole or in its total extent, and (ii) those which characterize a part or parts, but not the whole of it. Under (ii) are found certain 'evolutionary patterns', i.e. features which characterize several distinct segments of the process in such a way as to be repetitive or recurrent events. Under (i) are found 'large-scale features' of the process, six of which may be singled out for special mention.

(A) The evolutionary process as a whole is such that it has produced an overall or net increase in both the number of living things and the number of types (especially species) of living things on the earth. This increase has not been an uninterrupted tendency, to be sure, for there have been occasional, periodic reductions in numbers. Yet as the ascent of life continued the total quantity of protoplasm and of organic types became progressively larger. Lotka (1945) has even suggested that this is a basic law of the evolutionary process. Whatever may be thought of the suggestion, there can be no doubt that organic increase has occurred during life's history.

(B) The course of evolution has resulted in an overall or net increase in (i) the size, and (ii) the structural and functional complexity of organisms. The first forms of life were almost certainly microscopic, or at least very minute, if as is now conjectured, they were rudimentary genes ('protogenes') whose size was approximately of the molecular order (Cf. Muller, 1957; Wright, 1949). When compared with many later forms, they were also relatively simple in both their internal organization and their modes of functioning. A majority of these later forms show an increase in gross bodily size as well as in the intricacy of their anatomy and physiology. It is true that cases are known where descendants are actually smaller in size than their ancestors. Yet, for the most part, the evolutionary process has led to an enlarging and a complicating of organisms (Cf. Sherrington, 1953).

(C) Not only were the earliest forms of life relatively small and uncomplicated, but they were also adapted to, and intimately dependent on, the specific environments in which they existed. Some later forms, however, have achieved a more generalized type of adaptation which enables them to cope with a range of environments. They have a greater degree of flexibility of response to the world than their remote ancestors and an increased independence of the changes going on in their immediate surroundings. In short, these later organisms are biologically 'more efficient' than the earliest ones. This feature depends on increased complexity of organization, and harmonious integration of parts, as well as on the development of various homeostatic mechanisms, e.g. a device for temperature-regulation. The evolution of the fore-brain and the central nervous system in vertebrates was of the utmost importance in making possible greater plasticity of behaviour and better control of the body. In the case of one evolutionary product, *Homo sapiens*, the intensification and improvement of mental capacities, combined with ability to use tools, led to an unprecedented power to manipulate the environment and make it serve his needs. Evolution, then, has produced beings whose all-round biological efficiency is superior to anything found at the early stages of life's history (Cf. Huxley, 1942, 1953; Thoday, 1953). Whether one is entitled to go a step further and talk about evolutionary 'progress' is a question which may be reserved for a subsequent point in the inquiry.

(D) As the course of evolution has continued, organisms have successively occupied an increasing number of different environments on the earth. Whenever any region of the physical world came to possess the minimal properties required to support life, some type of plant or animal nearly always proceeded to occupy and adapt itself to that region. Today one rarely finds an environmental niche where organisms could exist which does not in fact contain them. Moreover, when a new region has been occupied, the very presence in it of one type of population paves the way for other types to occupy it also. Consequently, not only does evolution show a surprising 'opportunism' in exploiting the possibilities of the physical environment to a maximum degree, but additional possibilities are created by living forms themselves.

(E) Every student of the paleontological evidence is bound to be impressed by another feature of the evolutionary process, namely the elimination or extinction of populations. As a paleontologist investigates older geological levels, not only does he encounter fewer recent species, but he observes that types of organisms now extinct were once abundant and apparently able to maintain themselves for substantial periods of time. These extinct types are sometimes called 'evolution's unsuccessful experiments'. The designation is not particularly apt, since some of the types can be said to have been highly 'successful' in the environmental conditions which prevailed while they were alive. Yet there is certainly a significant difference between those lines of descent which have continued for millions of years down to the present, and those which literally came to a dead end.

A useful distinction has been drawn between three different cases where the term 'extinction' is appropriately employed (Cf. Simpson, 1949). In the first case we have the disappearance of an ancestral form because of its transformation into a different form. Since it has no existing representatives, the ancestral form can be described as 'extinct'. The second case is where one group comes to replace an earlier group in a particular environmental niche. The replacement may occur without an intervening lapse of time, or it may be deferred in such a way that the niche remains unoccupied for a considerable period after the original group has disappeared. The third case is where a group is eliminated and no subsequent replacement occurs. This is extinction in the fullest sense, 'an apparent negation of the principle of increase, leaving a void in the expanding mass of life' (Simpson, 1949, 119).

Now it is a striking fact that as far as the multitude of minor types of organisms are concerned, extinction in one or other of the above senses has been a much more frequent occurrence than survival. The fossil evidence shows that for such organisms elimination from the evolutionary process is the rule rather than the exception. On the other hand, it is equally striking that none of the major or basic types of animal organization (i.e. the basic phyla) has ever become extinct. Large fluctuations in the number of their respective representatives have certainly occurred. But from Cambrian times, when these basic types of animal organization arose, down to the present, some representatives of each of the types have always existed. These two facts are important for any theory which seeks to formulate the causes of the evolutionary process.

(F) The last large-scale feature we will note concerns the rate at which populations have evolved. The task of determining the tempo of evolution is one which presents technical difficulties to the biologist. So far the investigation has been carried on mainly in terms of structural changes in animals, and to a lesser degree in terms of the diversification of types within species. The results of the investigation point to the conclusion that there is no such thing as *the* rate of evolution (Simpson, 1949). Different animal populations evolve at widely different rates during a given epoch; and a given animal population may display great variations in its rate of change during successive epochs. We ought not to think of evolution as though it were a river whose current has the same speed throughout the whole of its course. As Simpson remarks, the question 'How fast has evolution occurred?' is meaningless unless we specify what group of organisms, which of their structures, and what period in their history we are talking about. Certain other facets of this matter will be mentioned in Section 7 of the present chapter.

Summing up, we may say that the evidence assembled by paleontology together with various hypotheses and assumptions enable us to reconstruct the large-scale features of the evolutionary process. From the reconstruction we conclude that the process as a whole has been biogenetic, differentiating, enlarging, complicating, productive of increased efficiency, opportunistic, eliminative, and variable in rate. If we employ the visual model of a tree or a river delta to symbolize the history of all the populations which have inhabited the earth, we can say in addition that evolution has been 'branching' or 'radiating'. Such designations are no more than shorthand devices which summarize large-scale features of evolution. They simply help us to describe those features and imply nothing about the causes which were at work. Furthermore, the description is qualitative in character. We will next consider a development in biological theory which has made available certain devices for supplementing a qualitative description with one which is quantitative.

5. STATISTICAL MODELS OF EVOLUTION

During the past few decades students of population genetics have constructed certain mathematical or statistical models designed to show in an abstract way how evolution takes place. These models presuppose the principles of genetics formulated during the last one hundred years; and it is assumed that these principles have been operative in the evolutionary process from the beginning. The details of the models are mathematically complex. But it is not necessary for us to explore their technicalities. All we require is an outline of how the models function and how they represent the historical aspect of evolution.

First of all we must consider briefly the way geneticists view the world of living things. Each individual organism is regarded as a dynamic union of two constituents: a *phenotype* and a *genotype*. This distinction, as Dobzhansky remarks (1951, 20), is 'basic for clear thinking about biological problems.' An organism's phenotype consists of all its observable characters, i.e. its external form, internal structure, and various functions. These supply the subject-matter for such special sciences as morphology, anatomy, embryology, physiology, etc. An organism's genotype consists of the hereditary constitution which it has received from its ancestors. This constitution is a system of discrete factors (genes and chromosomes). The factors are arranged in a certain determinate pattern in each individual genotype. Because of the process of biparental reproduction, factors are transmitted in different combinations from parents to offspring, so that, with a few minor exceptions, each individual organism has a unique genotype which differentiates it from every other individual. It would be a little more precise to say that (save for the minor exceptions) the probability of any two members of a population possessing the same set of genetic factors in the same combination is extremely small.

Now the phenotypic characters of an individual organism are the joint product of its genotype interacting with the particular environment in which the organism has existed from the moment of its origin. The phenotype is not just a mechanical expression of the genotype, as some have thought. What the genotype does is to determine a range of potential characters which can be engendered in all possible environments. The set of characters *actually* realized by an organism depends also on the particular environment occupied by it. We should not forget that the genotype exerts its determining action through developmental or embryological processes, so that, as de Beer has said, 'behind the simple phrase "a gene controlling this, that, or the other character", there is a complex embryological history to unravel' (de Beer, 1951, 220). Waddington (1942; 1953) has contended that the system of developmental processes is so important that it merits a special name, and he proposes the designation 'epigenotype'. He then comments: 'Changes in genotypes only have ostensible effects in evolution if they bring with them alterations in the epigenetic processes by which phenotypes come into being; and the kinds of change possible in the adult form of an animal are limited to the possible alterations in the epigenetic system by which it is produced' (Waddington, 1953, 190-91).

The controlling activity of genotypes is of special importance from the standpoint of evolution. For phenotypic characters as such are not transmitted from parents to offspring. What is transmitted is a complex of potentialities for development, determined by a set of genetic factors; and the specific potentialities actualized as phenotypic characters require the action of a specific environment. Furthermore, when as occasionally happens, a change or 'mutation' occurs in one of the genetic factors making up the genotype, there follows a change in some of the phenotypic characters of the individual or individuals concerned. If the individuals survive and reproduce, the new characters will tend to reappear in their descendants, provided the environment remains fairly stable.

It is possible, at least in principle, to trace the complete history of a population by noting all the phenotypic and genotypic differences among its members in successive generations. A comparison of an earlier stage of the population's history with a later one, if it disclosed some differences between ancestors and descendants, would provide a basis for asserting that the population had evolved. The tempo of evolution, as we have mentioned, is by no means constant. Nor is the occurrence of sudden, large differences necessarily excluded, although this is apparently quite rare. But in general it is true to say that the evolution of a population is the gradual, continuous change of phenotype and genotype in its individual members through successive generations. This process is sometimes called 'micro-evolution' because it is exemplified by the basic evolutionary units (populations) and involves at each stage only small-scale differences.

Statistical models of this process are constructed in roughly the following way. Since evolution is at bottom a change undergone by populations; and since a population is made up of individual organisms; and since the phenotypic characters of each organism are controlled by a unique genotype; and since each genotype is a system of discrete units which are transmitted in varying combinations from one generation to the next—it is possible to treat a population abstractly as a collection of these units. Instead of being considered an assemblage of individual organisms, or of individual genotypes, the population is regarded as an assemblage of genes (or pairs of genes). To each of these genetic units a number can be assigned which represents the frequency of its occurrence in the population. The resulting model manifests a certain pattern of gene frequencies, and the statistical alteration of this pattern is the process of microevolution. Hence we can describe evolution at the elementary level *as a non-random or systematic change of the gene frequencies in a population* (Dobzhansky, 1951; Medawar, 1951; Wright, 1945).

This model is illuminating for several reasons. It provides a quantitative framework which allows a number of observations and inferences to be brought into a coherent scheme. By utilizing laws known to govern the transmission of genetic units from parents to offspring (when abstraction from all environmental influences is made), the model permits a formal study of how gene frequencies behave under a variety of assumed environmental conditions. Such a formal study shows *inter alia* that certain kinds of evolutionary change can *not* take place under certain conditions because of restrictions imposed by the Mendelian laws of inheritance. The statistical model makes clear the fact that while evolutionary forces act on individual organisms, the effects of these forces are manifested not in individuals but in populations. Finally, the model shows that population changes are not chaotic but display definite patterns amenable to quantitative treatment. A valuable supplement to the qualitative description of evolution is thus provided.

At the same time, it is important to remember that the conclusions reached on the basis of the statistical model are not inductive or empirical generalizations. These conclusions are deductions which become empirically significant only when interpreted in the light of the results of experimental and field studies. For the model is constructed with the aid of a number of assumptions which enormously simplify the complex conditions existing in nature. Thus, it is assumed that a standard condition in a population is that of random interbreeding. Frequently, the constancy of the environment is postulated; and so on. Furthermore, the model also requires acceptance of the proposition that variation in a phenotypic character through successive generations of a population is controlled by the genotypic factors which are operative. This proposition is not susceptible of rigorous proof (Cf. Lerner, 1950). Indeed, it has been argued that there are facts which cast grave doubt upon it (Cf. 'Espinasse, 1952). But unless it is accepted, the statistical model cannot be made to work. For the proposition in question provides a basis for one of two steps which have to be taken in order to translate statements about gene frequencies into statements about populations. The other step is made possible by a mathematical theorem established in 1908 by Hardy and Weinberg, which allows statements about gene frequencies in a population to be translated into statements about the individual genotypes present in members of the population.

We may conclude, then, that while the statistical representation of evolution is a highly abstract way of characterizing it, the representation does bring out important aspects of the evolutionary process. Until recently, these aspects were quite unknown to biologists. The statistical representation also illuminates the manner in which the causes of evolution work, as we shall note later on. Despite all this, the achievements of 'evolutionary mathematics' should not be exaggerated (Cf. Waddington, 1953). Thus, when it is said that evolution is a statistical change in the genetics of populations, such that the proportion of genes and gene-sets is altered, we need to be aware that such a description may be limited to the basic levels of the evolutionary process, e.g. to local populations and perhaps to species. Whether the description applies to other phases of the process, e.g. the evolution of families, classes, orders, etc, is less easily decided. To appreciate a few of the issues that arise here, we must turn next to the question of the status of these 'higher' categories of living things.

6. SPECIES AND THE HIGHER CATEGORIES

It has already been noted that the evolutionary process has resulted in a net increase in the different kinds of organisms which have lived on the earth. The classification of these kinds, as they are known at present, is the special province of taxonomy or systematics. The classificatory scheme used by taxonomists contains a large number of categories, the most important of which are kingdom, phylum, class, order, family, genus and species (Simpson, 1945). These categories are arranged in a hierarchy so that as one proceeds from species to kingdom the successive stages involve an increasing extension and a decreasing closeness of relationship of the organisms classified. When the numerous subdivisions of the classificatory scheme are taken into account, the pattern becomes extremely intricate. But for our purpose it is sufficient to observe only its hierarchical structure. This can be graphically illustrated by the fact that whereas there are somewhere in the vicinity of one million and a half species of organisms, there are about twenty phyla and only two (or perhaps three) kingdoms.

Now the question may be asked whether these taxonomic categories represent natural groupings in the domain of living things. Differences of opinion exist about the proper answer to this question. Some taxonomists hold that each category represents a natural grouping or separate biological entity existing in rerum natura. Others hold that each category is nothing but a mental construct or arbitrary device for dealing in certain ways with individual organisms. On the former view, for instance, 'Arthropoda' is the name of a distinct morphological unit; on the latter view, this expression is not a name at all but a useful fiction. Between these two extremes a continuous range of possible positions occurs. One which has a good deal of support is that the lower categories of the hierarchical scheme, especially 'species', do denote fairly distinct biological entities which actually exist in nature. The higher categories, however, do not name such units, and hence may be regarded as 'less real' than the lower ones. Nevertheless, the higher categories do have *some* basis in the characteristics exhibited by organisms, and are therefore not properly regarded as arbitrary fictions. Perhaps the majority of systematists would agree that there is 'greater biological reality corresponding to the term species than to higher systematic units such as genus, family, or order' (Huxley, 1942, 167).

It would require too large a diversion from our main theme to embark on a discussion of this topic (Cf. Gilmour, 1940). We will, therefore, adopt the view that the main taxonomic categories, at least, have *some* 'biological reality', and are not convenient fictions. In other words, we will assume that taxonomic classification has an objective basis in the organisms classified, without attempting to specify in detail what the basis is. We can then ask what relations, if any, hold between the hierarchical structure of the classificatory scheme and the historical course of evolution. Certainly, as Mayr (1942) has pointed out, no taxonomic system can represent the course of phylogeny exactly; but still, the correlation seems to be close enough to permit the following questions to be asked. Was it the case that the evolution of populations gave rise first to species, then to genera, then to families, orders, classes, and phyla in that sequence? Or were populations from the start divided into phyla, so that the higher categories (phyla, classes, orders) were historically the earliest, and subsequently gave rise to lower and lower categories by a process of splitting? Any account of the historical aspect of evolution can scarcely avoid taking stock of these questions.

No special difficulty would arise if the evidence were such as to make a decisive answer possible. But the paleontological material is fragmentary and inconclusive at this point. Consequently, a direct settlement of the matter is out of the question and only considerations of an indirect nature are available. Hence, it is scarcely surprising to find diversity of opinion on the issue among biologists, though it seems fair to say that there is a minority and a majority party. We may, therefore, take note of their respective positions.

The minority party, represented by such eminent figures as Goldschmidt (1952), Schindewolf (1936) and Willis (1940), takes the view that evolution 'works down' from the higher categories to the lower, rather than from lower to higher. Goldschmidt has put the logic of this view clearly in the following passage.

'Looking at the taxonomic order of animals and plants, we see the picture represented as a pedigree or tree of descent. This means that a phylum consists of a number of classes all of which are basically recognizable as belonging to the phylum but, in addition, are different from each other. The same principle is repeated at each taxonomic level. All the genera of a family have in common the traits which characterize the family . . . but among themselves they differ from genus to genus. So it goes on down to the level of species. Can this mean anything but that the type of the phylum was evolved first and later separated into the types of the classes, then into orders, and so on down the line? This natural naïve interpretation of the existing hierarchy of forms actually agrees with the historical facts furnished by paleontology. The phyla existing today can be followed farthest back into remote geological time. Classes are a little younger, still younger are the orders, and so on until we come to the recent species which appear only in the latest geological epochs. Thus logic as well as historical fact tells us that the big categories existed first, and that in time they split in the form of the genealogical tree into lower and still lower categories' (Goldschmidt, 1952, 91-92).

A further consideration adduced in support of this view is the paucity of intermediate types or 'missing links' between the phyla of the animal kingdom. Responsibility for this can hardly be attributed to the imperfection of the geological record, since within various phyla remarkably complete series of types have been found (Needham, 1946). Hence, it is argued, the odds strongly favour the conclusion that no such intermediate types existed. Their absence is proof of the irreducible discontinuity of the evolutionary process.

A general consequence of this position is that evolution was from the start polyphyletic. At the time of the origin of living things on the earth, there must have arisen rather rapidly some representative or representatives of all, or virtually all, the phyla. This contemporaneous origin of the major groups was followed by an elaborate splitting which produced in successive geological ages the array of families, genera, and species known at present (Cf. Clark, 1930). Incidentally, no doctrine of special creation is presupposed here; though, as we have noted, Darwin supposed that life had originally been 'breathed by the Creator into a few forms or into one.' Most defenders of a polyphyletic beginning of evolution, however, not only exclude non-natural creation, but assume that more than just a few forms existed at the outset. Thus, Berg (1926) postulates 'a large number, thousands and possibly tens of thousands of primary germs' which evolved parallel to each other, were then extensively subject to extinction, and ultimately gave rise to the basic phyla. These proceeded to evolve in the manner represented by our present-day hierarchy of categories. Hence, evolution must have been 'from higher to lower'; though Berg himself never puts the matter in just this way.

The counter-position on the question of where the higher categories belong in evolution is represented by those who follow the broad tradition of Darwin, that is to say, by the majority of biologists. They reject the idea of a rapid, contemporaneous emergence of phyla as incompatible with the gradual changes known to characterize most of the evolutionary process. For these biologists, the diversity of organic types stems ultimately from the dividing of populations. The basic form of division produces reproductively isolated populations which can then be classified (in most cases) as distinct species. Since changes in one cannot be passed on to the others, their evolutionary histories will differ. In time, each population will divide; and through a repetition of this process, larger and larger groups of more or less similar species will result. These groups can then be formally classified as genera, families, orders, etc, in the standard hierarchical scheme.

Now it is clear from this account that the taxonomist's recognition and naming of a higher category, as well as his placing of it in the hierarchy, is *ex post facto* (Simpson, 1953). He is con-

D

fronted with an enormous array of populations existing in nature. By sampling these populations, he aims to express in his classificatory scheme the kind and degree of relationship which they have to one another. The most convenient device available consists of characters which the populations have in common, the character in each case representing an average or statistical feature of the population. Very often, the character belonged to a population which was ancestral to the ones being classified, though this is by no means necessary.

Yet according to the position we are now considering, it is incorrect to suppose '(1) that the characters-in-common are somehow a picture of the common ancestor which was a "generalized" organism without the sorts of "specialized" characters that distinguish its various descendants from each other; and (2) that the higher category arose as such when an organism acquired the given characters-in-common' (Simpson, 1953, 342). Both these doctrines arise from a failure to grasp the logic of classification, a failure due to the influence of tacit and unwarranted philosophical preconceptions. Chief among the latter is the belief that the classification of organisms must be based on certain ideal forms or 'archetypes' which exist in their own right and with which individual organisms are compared. This 'platonistic' outlook is incompatible with the actual practice of most modern taxonomists. For them a taxonomic category is not a standard of comparison, but 'only a needed device for legalistic nomenclatural purposes' (Simpson, 1953, 341).

What this *ex post facto* view of the higher categories involves may be further displayed by means of an example. It is customary to classify domesticated and wild horses, asses, and zebras as different species of the genus *Equus*, since they have numerous characters-in-common. It is also customary to recognize that these animals have a common ancestor in the long extinct *Eohippus*, which, together with the members of *Equus* and all the intermediate types, constitute the family *Equidae*. But when *Eohippus* lived *there was no such family*. It would not have been possible at that stage of evolution to describe *Eohippus* as 'a horse-like mammal'. We can describe it thus *now* because we recognize it as the ancestor of what subsequently became the diverse species of *Equus*. Moreover, as far as can be determined by the fossil record, *Eohippus* did not have any of the characters-in-common used by taxonomists in classifying the species of *Equus*. In short, 'the family and all its distinctive characters developed gradually as time went on ... there is no particular time at which the *Equidae* became a family rather than a genus or species; the whole process was gradual and we assign the categorical rank after the result is before us' (Simpson, 1953, 345). This is the sense in which it is true to say that the higher categories evolved later than the lower ones.

Although the formulation here is impressive, it is worth noting a hostile criticism brought forward by Goldschmidt (1952). Taking as an illustration the alleged process by which the class of birds evolved from the class of reptiles, he argues that no really cogent account of the process is forthcoming in neo-Darwinian terms. For these terms require that the basic changes must always take place at the lowest or subspecific level. Hence the line of evolution in the present case must have started with a subspecific population belonging to the class *Reptilia*. The accumulation of small differences or mutations in this population transformed it into a new species. More accumulation of small differences made it a new genus, then a new family, a new order, and finally a new class, viz. *Aves*. But then, 'After the first bird had evolved by the divergence of more and more accumulated mutants along some reptile line, this new form must then have started to build up subspecies which diverged into species, and so on until all the orders, families, genera, etc, of birds had been diversified. But all of them remained birds while formerly the same process had made birds out of reptiles. Such are the workings of evolution according to the neo-Darwinian scheme!' (Goldschmidt, 1952, 52). The best alternative to this incomprehensible doctrine, Goldschmidt holds, is his own view that 'the big categories existed first', and gave rise to the lower categories by repeated splitting and divergence.

A philosopher surveying the pros and cons of this controversy finds himself in no position to espouse one side rather than the other. The only reasonable conclusion seems to be that considerations so far advanced do not permit a settlement. It is always tempting under such circumstances to suppose that the original question may have been wrongly put or that it lacks empirical meaning. Neither supposition is plausible in the present instance. For we certainly know what sort of observations would allow us to arrive at an answer; and, indeed, we already have at least one example, inconclusive though it is, of the type of observation required (i.e. that the paleontological record shows few, if any, continuous sequences between the higher categories). We may, therefore, conclude that we are faced here with a meaningful and answerable, but so far unanswered, question.

If such is the case, we must further conclude that the statistical conception outlined in the previous section is not known to apply to *every* part of the evolutionary process. The conception provides a valuable model in the light of which we can understand what takes place when local populations change and give rise to species. In other words, the model helps us to understand microevolution, or the elementary form of phylogenesis. Yet because of the disagreement about how the higher categories evolve, it must be regarded as uncertain whether the model is relevant to the understanding of these upper levels. Accordingly, we are *not* entitled to say that *evolution as a whole* is a statistically describable process, since this goes beyond anything biologists have been able to establish.

Whether the higher categories arose suddenly at the beginning of evolution, or whether they arose gradually out of repeated changes at lower levels as evolution went on, is a historical issue. It has, therefore, not involved the discussion of any causal questions. We have not inquired, for instance, whether the higher categories came into being as a result of the same causal factors which were operative in the case of the lower categories; or whether some additional factor or factors must be recognized as causally determinative of the upper levels of the taxonomic hierarchy. This issue will come up for discussion in the ensuing chapter. There is no intrinsic connection between the causal and the historical questions. For one might hold that the higher categories were preceded in time by the lower categories, and yet consider that the appearance of the former cannot be causally explained in terms of the same factors which account for the origin of species. In other words, one might agree with the contention regarding the historical priority of the lower categories, but disagree with the broad Darwinian account of the causes of phyla, classes, etc. Before turning to this question we will bring the chapter to a close by taking note of some of the recurrent patterns which occur in evolution.

7. SOME EVOLUTIONARY PATTERNS

Everybody who writes about evolution needs to be on guard against two dangers. The first is oversimplifying the facts. The second is making unwarranted generalizations. Living things are so incredibly complex in their organization and functioning that a simple formula rarely applies to them. Their history is so multifarious and incompletely known that almost every generalization has exceptions. When we come to the subject of evolutionary patterns, i.e. sequences of events which are recurrent, these dangers are perhaps slightly less acute. For from this standpoint evolution is not so much a single process, as an intertwining of many processes. It is not uniform but multiform, a heterogeneity rather than a homogeneity. We will now single out a few important recurrent patterns which have been discerned, and thereby take cognizance of the multiformity of evolution.

A convenient division of these patterns can be made by distinguishing the following occurrences (Cf. Rensch, 1947; Simpson, 1953). (A) Within a population, steady cumulative change may occur, often for long stretches of time, and yet no marked alteration of the basic adaptive type will arise. This is what Simpson calls 'phyletic evolution'. (B) Differentiation may proceed within a population to the point where a new species arises. This is the phenomenon of 'speciation'. (C) There may occur an extensive diversification of a given type of organism (species, genus, etc), by branching or forking, usually in a single adaptive zone. This constitutes the phenomenon known as 'splitting' (Simpson) or 'cladogenesis' (Rensch). It should not be thought that these are three absolutely independent phases of evolution. For while under certain circumstances (A) may occur by itself, it commonly leads to (B) and (C). Similarly, (B) seems to require (A) but not necessarily (C); while (C) presupposes (A) but does not necessarily involve (B). With this reminder of the interconnections of the three occurrences, we may take note of the recurrent patterns in each of them separately.

(A) A fundamental recurrent pattern of phyletic evolution must clearly be the statistical transformation of populations discussed in Section 5 above. Enough has been said about this for present purposes. It may well be that the statistical model is applicable to the very earliest stage of the evolutionary process, as well as to subsequent ones. Wright (1949) has suggested that the first populations of autocatalytic, nucleo-protein molecules or proto-genes, were governed by factors which the model represents. Quite apart from this suggestion, there is little doubt that the statistical pattern has been exemplified on an immense number of occasions in evolutionary history.

Other recurrent patterns of phyletic evolution are connected with the fact that it requires the maintenance in ancestral and descendant populations of adaptation to the environment. Among the numerous items here we may single out the following as of special interest.

(i) In an environment which remains relatively stable for a long time, organisms may undergo little or no change because their existing adaptation is adequate. The 'tempo' of their evolu-tion is slow or 'bradytelic' (Simpson, 1944). A limiting case is provided by the so-called 'arrested evolution' of some organisms (e.g. *Latimeria, Lingula*, etc) which have remained virtually un-altered for millions of years.

(ii) At the other end of the scale is the pattern of short range, rapid evolution associated with the maintenance of adaptation to drastic environmental changes (e.g. the climatic revolution at the end of the Cretaceous Period), or with the wholesale shift of a group of organisms from an ancestral adaptive zone to a new one which happens to become available. This somewhat rare process has been called 'tachytelic' or 'quantum' evolution (Simpson, 1944; 1953). By means of it a group moves *en masse* from one zone to the other with maximum speed, leaving behind few transitional forms.

(iii) Intermediate between these two extremes is the most typical pattern of phyletic evolution, viz. long range, cumulative change in a group of organisms. This may be due to the main-taining of adequate adaptation to a slowly altering environment, or it may be due to the perfecting of adaptation to a relatively stable environment (i.e. to increasing specialization). There may also be cases where such long-range changes are non-adaptive, or where it is difficult to show their adaptive significance.

The chief form in which this recurrent pattern manifests itself is that of evolutionary trends. A trend is a prolonged series of changes of the same sort in an observable character (or characters) of a group of organisms (e.g. increase of average bodily size or of the height of teeth). Such changes are normally manifested in a sequence of fossils. Although it is impossible to specify exactly how prolonged a sequence must be in order to be designated a 'trend', not less than one million years would seem to be required (Cf. Simpson, 1953). Some trends are considerably longer.

It is usual to say that such changes occur in a 'single direction'. When they are undeviating, the trend may be described as 'rectilinear'. These expressions are intended to convey the fact that a trend is a non-random sequence of events which takes place as if a predetermined goal were being sought from the outset of the sequence. Certain biologists, indeed, have held that a special directing agency, internal or external, must be at work in all evolutionary trends. This is the doctrine of 'orthogenesis', which has been the focal point of extensive controversy (Cf. Jepsen, 1949). Since it introduces the issue of causality into the discussion, I will postpone consideration of it until the next chapter. There can be no objection, of course, to using the term 'orthogenetic' in a descriptive sense, as a way of referring to long-term trends, provided this usage is made explicit.

The fossil evidence, then, shows that orthogenetic trends are of frequent occurrence in evolution. From the standpoint of paleontology, their detailed features are complex, and not for an amateur to discuss. One further general point may be noted, however, because it has a bearing on matters to be taken up later.

Paleontologists have observed that quite often different groups of organisms show in their evolution closely similar sequences of changes with respect to a given character or characters (e.g. the similar coiling of the shells in distinct populations of oysters of the genus Ostrea). Such trends are said to be 'parallel' if the lineages in which they occur are contemporaneous, and 'iterative' if the lineages arise successively (Simpson, 1953). The evidence suggests that the more closely the groups are related, the more likely it is that parallel or iterative trends will be found, and the greater the degree of similarity exhibited. Yet a few paleontologists have contended that these trends are also found in quite unrelated groups. This contention is by no means undisputed, but it does give rise to the question whether parallelism and iteration can be adduced as evidence of a directing agency in evolution which operates teleologically, or whether a plausible explanation in non-teleological terms can be provided. The existence of orthogenetic trends as recurrent patterns is not disputed by anyone who has looked at the evidence.

(B) We come next to patterns associated with the process of speciation. In this process two or more new species arise from a parent species. The time-span required has been estimated to be normally of the order of 1,000,000 years (Mayr, 1949a), the shortest time-span known being about 500,000 years (Cf. Zeuner, 1946). For this reason speciation is not a directly observable process but one which, like so many other aspects of evolution, is inferred. To grasp the central points in the patterns here it will be desirable to say something further about the meaning of the term 'species'.

As previously mentioned, no one has succeeded in framing a definition of this term which is acceptable to all biologists. Indeed, the phenomena such a definition would have to embrace are so diverse that the task of framing it seems almost hopeless. The most promising line of attack in recent years is one which substitutes a phylogenetic conception for the archetypal conceptions of classical taxonomy. In other words, it proposes to find a criterion of species in the domain of evolving populations.

The core of the phylogenetic approach is as follows. If two or more natural populations of bi-parental animals are such that their constituent individuals are able to interbreed and produce fully fertile offspring, then the populations form or are parts of a single species. On the other hand, if two or more natural populations are such that their constituent individuals cannot interbreed, or do so only in rare instances, then the populations form or are parts of distinct species. The criterion appealed to here is that of reproductive isolation. When there is no such isolation, specific differences are absent; and when isolation obtains specific differences are nearly always found. Hence, 'species are groups of actually or potentially interbreeding natural populations, which are reproductively isolated from other such groups' (Mayr, 1942, 120). The great virtue of the appeal to reproductive isolation is that reference is made to a discontinuity or gap existing in nature. The gap prevents any interchange of hereditary factors between the members of the respective populations, and thus sets up a sharp line of demarcation which enables biologists to say that 'species are tangible natural phenomena' (Dobzhansky, 1951, 263).

Certain qualifications have to be added immediately so as to avoid misunderstanding. Mayr's statement is not, and does not profess to be, a *definition* of 'species'. It simply formulates a criterion in terms of a condition which is widely fulfilled in the case of bisexual animals, though not in the case of plants. Furthermore, the species which this criterion allows us to single out are not necessarily identical with the species studied by taxonomy. The taxonomist is chiefly interested in morphological features of organisms, and uses as his criteria for distinguishing two different species the salient morphological differences and the absence of intergrading (i.e. the absence of forms intermediate in structure between the species). Such species, however, are essentially static, whereas the use of the criterion of reproductive isolation implies a dynamic conception of a species as a stage or phase of the on-going evolutionary process.

On the latter approach, speciation takes place when various agencies set up barriers to reproduction between two or more sub-groups of members of a population. Interbreeding and the exchange of genetic material between the groups gradually diminishes to zero. As a result, differentiation occurs and two or more species arise. If they are to co-exist in the same locality, these species must be sufficiently different in their ecological needs to keep interspecific competition from becoming too intense. Acordingly, 'speciation . . . means the evolution of reproductive isolation as well as of ecological differentiation between populations' (Mayr, 1949a, 515). It will be apparent that this process involves the multiplication of species, since one population gives rise to two more. Hence the case where an isolated population (e.g. on a remote island) undergoes prolonged, gradual changes so that the descendants are judged to constitute a species different from their ancestors, is not strictly an example of speciation. Here no increase in the number of existing species has resulted. But such prolonged, gradual change is, as we have seen, characteristic of phyletic evolution.

The diversity of the patterns of speciation is a technical matter into which we do not need to enter. It springs mainly from the various isolating mechanisms which reduce, and ultimately prevent, the exchange of genetic material between populations. These mechanisms have been classified in several ways by recent investigators (Cf. Mayr, 1942; Allee, et al., 1949; Dobzhansky, 1951). But there is full agreement about the vital rôle they play in speciation.

(C) The final recurrent pattern we will mention is related to, yet distinct from, the multiplication of species. It is the pattern of 'adaptive radiation' displayed in connection with the diversification of types of organisms during their evolution. According to Huxley (1942), the level at which this phenomenon appears most clearly is that of classes and sub-classes. But it can also be discerned, though not so sharply, in both higher and lower systematic units. The pre-conditions of adaptive radiation lie in phyletic evolution. That is to say, a group of organisms gradually changes until it arrives at a point in its history where it is about to enter upon a new phase and become a dominant, highly successful type of life. The point is marked by the availability of a new environmental niche or zone which is relatively unoccupied, and by the availability of the characters which the organisms need in order to exploit the new ecological opportunities to the full.

When such a situation prevails, the organisms do not just occupy the new zone broadly. They 'radiate' into it (Simpson, 1949). This means that they distribute themselves throughout the zone by sub-dividing or splitting into numerous groups each of which occupies some limited region within the zone and then proceeds to adapt itself to the special requirements of that region. The sub-division which takes place here is approximately contemporaneous, not successive. In this respect it differs from another phenomenon with which it intergrades, namely, the gradual occupation at different times of a variety of zones. 'The essence of adaptive radiation thus consists first in the invasion of different regions of the environment by different lines within a group, and secondly in their exploitation of different modes of life' (Huxley, 1942, 493). The original group branches out into a variety of adaptive types (including species), each of which develops its own particular specialization, and proceeds to colonize a separate part of the environment. In the initial stages of the process, the pace of evolution is nearly always rapid.

Some biologists distinguish a 'basic' or 'primary' radiation from 'secondary' and 'tertiary' radiations which are built upon it. Thus, the rise of the placental mammals is a primary radiation considered in relation to the secondary radiation of the primates within the mammalian class and to the tertiary radiation of the prosimians within the primate order. Again a hierarchical sequence is apparent. The link between any two stages of the hierarchy is generally formed by a single line stemming from the earlier radiation. This line represents the particular branch of that radiation which eventually proved to be superior to the rest. It survived and continued to evolve, whereas other branches of the radiation were either eliminated or became stabilized in a mode of life which precluded further transformation. If we think of this whole pattern by means of a diagram of a tree, then we should not imagine that each branch undergoes simple bifurcation. 'The diagram should rather consist of a series of many-branched divisions, each branch repeatedly dividing after its origin, and one of the branches leading to the next radiation' (Carter, 1951, 19). The 'tree of life' is not nearly as trim as some early Darwinians believed.

In the repeated phenomenon of adaptive radiation, living things have become progressively diversified and have progressively extended their activities into new regions. Whenever this phenomenon has occurred, some adaptive zone has been available to some type of organism. But since the number of such zones on the earth which can serve as possible abodes of life is limited, there has been a tendency for the scope of adaptive radiation to contract. 'As far as environmental possibilities go, the very broadest scope for adaptive radiation existed when life first arose, even though the further evolution of life has itself from time to time opened up very broad possibilities' (Simpson, 1953, 224). The situation at present is that the supply of suitable zones is small, and the opportunities offered by any one of them relatively insignificant. Hence there is some ground for inferring that the process of evolutionary diversification may be just about finished. Whether we can also infer that evolution as a whole must be just about finished is a matter we will discuss in the final chapter.

This completes my account of some of the things contemporary evolutionary theory has to say about the historical aspects of life. It cannot be too strongly emphasized that the points dealt with represent a selection from an extremely large collection of material. The selection has been made in the light of the two questions posed at the beginning of the chapter (What is it that evolves? and How does it evolve?); and also in the light of certain philosophical issues to be taken up later. But I have only brought under review the more important aspects of this whole subject.

CHAPTER III

CAUSAL ASPECTS OF EVOLUTION

1. THE PROBLEM OF EXPLAINING EVOLUTION CAUSALLY

Contemplation of the grand panorama depicted by evolutionary theory evokes in many minds a double response. There is first a feeling of wonder that a sequence of events so remarkable in its large-scale features and its details should have occurred at all. It is not easy to say why this feeling arises. One source, I think, is a sense of the colossal improbability of what has taken place. We can imagine ourselves viewing the terrestrial scene more than a thousand million years ago, when the sole living things were minute, relatively homogeneous entities, such as rudimentary genes, and being asked to estimate the likelihood of this primitive population giving rise to organisms as different as bacteria, mushrooms, ferns, sponges, jellyfish, earthworms, oysters, ants, hummingbirds, whales, turtles and human beings. Or one imagines being asked to say how likely it is that this primitive population will eventually split up into a million and a half species. In both cases one feels that the spontaneous answer would be 'Fantastically unlikely! Improbable to the point of impossibility!' Yet the evidence shows that this 'fantastic improbability' has occurred.

Another source of the feeling of wonder may be the recognition that despite the great diversity and complexity of living things, they fit into a single economy of nature. Every living thing is suited to the environment in which it exists, and the environment is suited to the requirements of the things which live in it. There are, to be sure, disharmonies. But the general effect is that of a well-arranged scheme, exhibiting a remarkable degree of design. If one turns from the overall effect to the detailed characters of animals and plants, one is further struck by the fact that nearly all these characters appear to serve some purpose in the life of the organism, enabling it to maintain itself for varying periods of time. This spectacle of design or purpose may be apparent, rather than real. But the fact remains that it is a spectacle at which students do not cease to marvel, even after long familiarity with it. Some have seen in it an interweaving of beauty and tragedy (Haldane, 1932a).

The second response evoked by contemplation of the panorama of evolution is a deep curiosity as to what brought it about. We are led to ask whether it is the result of a cause or set of causes which can be discovered by rational inquiry. The attempt to satisfy this curiosity has resulted in the framing of a number of explanatory theories, some scientific, others speculative. In the present chapter I will discuss chiefly the powerful scientific theory put forward by biologists who have espoused the modern selectionist or 'synthetic' point of view. This theory is an extension of the doctrine proposed by Darwin, and it contains many points of philosophical interest. In the course of surveying it certain other doctrines, as well as certain methodological matters, will be considered.

Before turning to any details I shall mention some of the items that stand in need of explanation. Two groups of them can be distinguished. The first group embraces historical phenomena such as were described in the preceding chapter. Among the items to be explained are (i) the occurrence of the overall course of evolution, as far as it has been reconstructed; (ii) the large-scale features which it has exhibited; (iii) its major recurrent patterns (e.g. speciation, adaptive radiation, extinction, etc); and (iv) major transitional episodes which have occurred in it (e.g. the origin of multicellular from unicellular organisms, the origin of terrestrial from aquatic forms, the derivation of birds from reptilian stock, etc). The second group of *explicanda* embraces a large body of phenomena derived from observation of organisms now on the earth. Here there are such items to be explained as the diversity, adaptations and fitness of living things, their geographical distribution, and the structural similarities (homologies), variations, vestiges, etc, which they manifest. Many of these phenomena are 'read back' into the historical record by assuming the truth of the 'uniformitarian principle', which affirms, roughly speaking, that at least part of the key to the past is to be found in the present (Cf. Simpson, Pittendrigh and Tiffany, 1957). Accordingly, an adequate explanatory theory will have to account for the presumed adaptations, fitness, etc, of past organisms as well as of organisms which now exist.

What form do explanations of the above phenomena take? Here it is important to recall a point alluded to in the opening chapter. The scientific theory of evolution, it was remarked, combines both systematic and historical modes of explanation. Systematic explanations contain abstract, non-empirical concepts by means of which law-like statements can be formulated. These statements refer to causal factors which are assumed to have been operative during the whole, or a large part, of the evolutionary process. The resulting explanations thus belong to a level of maximum generality within the framework of the theory. Most of the doctrines of the modern selectionist or synthetic theory are located on this level. To what extent, if any, exact predictions can be based on the law-like statements which occur here is a question I shall take up towards the end of the chapter.

At a lower level of the theory are to be found historical explanations. They are not just accidental items which reflect the theory's 'undeveloped' nature. On the contrary, they are essential to it, and have their foundation in the fact that organisms are literally historical creatures. Their history is built into them. Hence no scientific account of organisms can be satisfactory if it abstracts them from their concrete history (Cf. Pittendrigh, 1958). As I shall try to show, two sorts of historical explanation play an important part in evolutionary theory. The first sort has to do with some of the phenomena specified above as arising from investigations of living things now on the earth. The second sort has to do with the major transitional episodes whose occurrence is required by the total phylogenetic process. Neither of these types of explanation contain law-like statements. Hence neither of them can provide a basis for exact positive predictions. Yet both types appear to be causal, or at any rate to embody causal components.

One consequence of this interpretation is that the division of evolutionary theory into a historical part which is wholly descriptive ('natural history'), and a non-historical part which is wholly explanatory, does less than justice to the facts. A more adequate division is between the part of the theory which embraces historical reconstructions and explanations, and the part which embodies systematic explanations. The latter division is the one observed in the present study.

Since the idea of causality is going to play a vital part in the discussion, it is essential to make clear the meaning which the idea is understood to have. I will adopt the widely accepted view that 'causality' refers to a relation which holds between a condition, C, and what it conditions, E, such that C is temporally prior to or simultaneous with, but never temporally posterior to, E. If C is a single, unanalysable factor, there are three alternative possibilities. (i) C is a *necessary condition* of E; the absence of C ensures the absence of E. (ii) C is a *sufficient condition* of E; the presence of C ensures the presence of E. (iii) C is the *necessary and sufficient* condition of E. If, as is nearly always the case, C is a constellation of factors, other possibilities arise. (iv) Each of certain factors of the constellation, n_1, n_2, n_3, ... is a necessary condition of E. (v) The factors n_1, n_2, n_3, ... n_n are severally necessary and jointly sufficient conditions of E. In other words, *the* cause of E, is analysable without residue into n_1 & n_2 & n_3 ... & n_n. (vi) Each of certain factors, n_1, n_2, n_3 ... is a necessary condition of E; and each of c_1, c_2, c_3 ... is a contingent, contributory condition of E. The complete set of necessary conditions together with at least one contingent contributory condition, constitute a sufficient condition of E. That is to say, there are several different complex sufficient conditions, s_1, s_2, s_3 ... of E; or as it is usually put, 'a plurality of causes' of E. Each sufficient condition, however, must contain *all* of E's necessary conditions.

In the light of the above, the meaning of certain linguistic expressions may be specified. One might plausibly suppose that the expression 'the cause of evolution' must refer to case (iii). However, since it is certain that no one, unanalysable factor is the necessary and sufficient condition of the evolutionary process, this meaning of the expression can be excluded. Does the expression refer to case (v)? If we answer in the affirmative, we should have to say that the expression represents an ideal limit to which biological thought may indefinitely approximate. For it is highly dubious whether a finite set of factors could ever be shown to be severally necessary and jointly sufficient conditions of evolution. A somewhat less stringent ideal is embodied in case (vi). Here we can say that we have identified 'the cause of evolution' when we are able to specify a set of factors which constitutes a complex sufficient condition of the evolutionary process. I will adopt this less stringent interpretation in the present discussion. The expression 'a cause of evolution' will be used to designate any necessary condition of it, as in (i) and (iv). Lastly, the expression 'the causes of evolution' will be taken to refer to some ('the most important') necessary conditions of it. These formal distinctions will be put to use in the course of the investigation.

Two other comments of a methodological nature remain to be made. (*a*) It is now an accepted doctrine that a scientific theory must contain concepts which cannot be correlated with what is observed or observable. These concepts, sometimes called 'theoretical constructs', are abstract ideas which have no direct empirical interpretation. They nevertheless play an important rôle in the framework of the theory. Their scientific admissibility depends on the fact that they occur in statements which have a systematic or deductive connection with observation-statements which refer directly to empirical data. Because of this systematic connection, theoretical constructs have scientific meaning conferred on them. Observation-statements also provide the means whereby the theory as a whole is tested to ascertain its probable truth or falsity (Cf. Hempel, 1952). (*b*) There are strong reasons for holding that a theory is properly called 'scientific' provided it entails observation-statements which are capable of being *refuted* by any empirical data. For this guarantees that the theory is in principle falsifiable. The possibility is admitted that observations might turn up (although perhaps they never will) which would lead to the theory being rejected. On the other hand, a theory which has successfully resisted a long series of attempts to falsify it, is to be regarded as well-established and probably true (Cf. Popper, 1957a; 1959).

We may expect, then, that modern selectionist theory will contain a number of concepts which have no direct empirical interpretation. Without such concepts it could not perform its explanatory function. Yet they must be systematically connected through the statements in which they occur with concepts which refer to empirical data. One of our tasks will be to discover what some of these systematic connections are; although, in view of the impossibility of reconstructing the theory axiomatically, the connections will have to be indicated in an informal and incomplete way. The two methodological points mentioned in the preceding paragraph will also have a bearing on the appraisal of certain other explanatory theories which have tried to compete with modern selectionism.

One may hope, finally, that an adequate explanatory account of evolution will have some light to shed on the source of the feeling of wonder which the spectacle of evolution excites. By doing so it may allow us to see, for example, that given the set of conditions which it specifies, the evolutionary process is indeed 'highly improbable', and that given those conditions it was to be expected that the process should display apparent purpose in a large number of its details. Yet even if the theory does these things, it will not remove the feeling of wonder. The latter may even be intensified as a result of what is said.

2. HISTORICAL EXPLANATIONS IN EVOLUTIONARY THEORY

In this section I want to discuss the subject of the historical explanations which form part of evolutionary theory. Although they do not belong uniquely to the modern selectionist account of evolution, that account would certainly be inadequate without them. I have already mentioned that two sorts of historical explanation are of special significance. I will refer to them as 'integrating' and 'narrative' explanations respectively. Neither of them contains any law-like statements, yet each can be plausibly construed as causal. They will be taken up briefly in turn.

(A) Integrating Explanations

The combined inquiries of paleontology and historical geology, supplemented by various other special disciplines such as taxonomy, permit the broad outlines of the history of life on the earth to be reconstructed. As a result, what has taken place can be summed up in a general historical statement, an excellent example of which is the following:

'Living organisms are all related to each other and have arisen from a unified and simple ancestry by a long sequence of divergence, differentiation and complication from that ancestry' (Simpson, 1950b, v).

A statement of this sort is what many biologists have in mind when they talk about the 'fact' of evolution, or when they say 'evolution is not a theory but a fact'. Since, however, the word 'fact' is notoriously controversial, it seems wiser to regard the general statement as one to be accepted because (i) it is supported by a large, steadily increasing body of direct evidence (fossils); and (ii) it has no serious competitor in its particular field. More-

E

over, once accepted the statement can be used to *explain* a wide range of phenomena established by disciplines which study present-day organisms. These disciplines are integrated to the extent that the phenomena are shown to be explained by the statement, and the latter thereby receives additional, indirect support.

Illustrations of this state of affairs are readily available. Thus in comparative anatomy it is a commonplace that animals of widely separated species share similarities of bodily structure even when their ways of life are quite diverse. The flipper of a whale, the wing of a bat, the leg of a horse, and a human arm are structurally alike (i.e. homologous), although functionally quite different. Each represents a modification of a single basic pattern. Why is this? The answer given by modern biologists is 'that the similarity exists because the animals concerned *inherited* the structure from an ancestor which they shared in common. . . . When the descendants of this ancestor took to life in the water, to locomotion through the air, or to running over hard ground they made over what they had in the way of limbs to serve the new functions. But despite the reconstruction necessary the indelible traces of the inherited pattern still remain' (Moody, 1953, 24).

The logical form of this explanation is as follows. From a general historical statement (that all organisms are the outcome of descent with modification from common ancestors in the remote past) an inference can be made that phenomena of a certain sort (homologous structures) are to be expected. But the particular phenomenon cited (the homology exhibited in the whale's flipper, the bat's wing, the horse's leg and the human arm) is one of that sort. It is exactly what might have been expected. Hence it is accounted for by the general historical statement. Furthermore, since this statement has no serious competitor in its field, the explanation offered can be reinforced by posing a rhetorical question: Why should the particular homology cited be present unless it were the case that the animals involved had descended from a common ancestor? Or, to put it positively, unless the animals in question had descended from a common ancestry, it is difficult to understand why they should exhibit homologous structures. This same pattern of reasoning occurs in comparative embryology, comparative physiology and comparative biochemistry where basic similarities among organisms are given a historical explanation.

Another widespread phenomenon observed in the living world is the presence of vestiges. These are bodily parts which are relatively small in size and which have little, if any, ascertainable rôle in promoting the viability of their possessors. The parts represent useless remnants of structures or organs which are bigger and functionally effective in some other present-day organisms. Familiar examples are the vermiform appendix in man, rudimentary limbs in certain snakes, the wings of flightless birds, etc. How is the presence of such useless structures to be explained? 'To most biologists . . . the presence of small organs that seem to have no function in themselves but correspond to functional organs possessed by other animals indicates inheritance from a common ancestry. Descendants having use for the organ in question retained it as a functional organ; in descendants having no use for it the organ reduced in size. The culmination of the trend would be complete loss of the organ' (Moody, 1953, 42).

Here again the explanation offered is historical. It is, however, slightly more complex than the preceding one and may be reconstructed as follows: 'Most organs and structures observed in present-day animals have an adaptive function in relation to their way of life. By virtue of the uniformitarian principle, we infer that most organs and structures of past animals were likewise adaptive. Yet among present-day animals (and plants) vestiges are observed. Now the presence of these vestiges would be accounted for if they were inherited remains of organs and structures which once had an adaptive function in the lives of ancestral organisms. But we have plenty of evidence that such ancestral organisms existed; and it is reasonable to suppose that their adaptive needs, being different from those of their descendants, would require fully developed organs and structures of the sort now represented by vestiges. The presence of these vestiges is to be expected, given the general character of the history of life. Hence they are satisfactorily explained in terms of that history, together with certain assumptions which are plausible.'

The diverse phenomena of homologous structures and vestiges are integrated by means of the doctrine of descent with modification and inheritance from a common ancestry. Another group of phenomena upon which this kind of explanation has a bearing is established by biogeographers. They have observed that present-day flora and fauna are distributed on the earth in ways which at first seem surprising. Thus one would expect geographically similar regions, such as Africa south of the Sahara, South America and Australia, to support broadly similar animal populations. Yet this is not the case. Often a region which is ecologically suitable for a certain type of population may have few, if any, representatives of that type native to the region (e.g. placental mammals in Australia). Large groups of related animals are limited to special regions of the globe, but not always because those regions are the only places where the animals could live. Why should the giraffe family be restricted to Africa? Why are tigers found in India but not in Africa? Why are armadillos found mainly in South America? All such questions about the *de facto* distribution of organisms demand an answer which will explain what is observed to be the case.

'The answer is to be found in the past, in the history of evolving life in relation to the history of the seas and continents' (Wells, Huxley and Wells, 1931, 390-91). From paleontology and historical geology it is possible to infer a great deal about the distribution of flora and fauna in past epochs. It is also possible to infer a great deal about the connection or separation of the large land-masses and bodies of water during those epochs. The existence of land-bridges which permitted migrations, of barriers such as seas, broad deserts, high mountains, etc, which produced isolation, of drastic alterations of climate, and so on, can be mapped on the geological time-scale. Then by using the doctrine of phylogenetic descent (supplemented by various special hypotheses such as that of dispersal from a common centre), plausible explanations can be devised for a number of the phenomena of biogeography. Since this field of inquiry is complex, not to mention controversial, the precise content of these explanations need not concern us. It is enough to note that they undertake to show how existing states of affairs are the result of the combined action of sequences of past events.

Integrating explanations of the above sort do their job without the aid of any general laws. The explanations are 'non-nomological'. Because of this fact they provide no basis for making exact, positive predictions. Present phenomena are explained by showing them to be the outcome of past sequences of phenomena; but nothing is deducible here about phenomena yet to come. Furthermore, these explanations are amenable to evaluation. Their biological satisfactoriness or unsatisfactoriness can be determined. Hence they have every right to be called 'scientific'. They constitute a legitimate and unavoidable move in formulating evolutionary theory. Yet their presence calls for an amendment of the common view that every scientific explanation must have predictive value. There are many occasions in the sciences (e.g. in classical mechanics), to be sure, where the explanation of a phenomenon is accomplished by deriving it from general laws which link it with antecedent conditions, and where these same laws are sufficient to allow prediction of the phenomenon, given those conditions. In such nomological explanations, there is a symmetry with respect to explanatory and predictive functions. However, this is not true of *all* scientific explanations, as evolutionary theory makes abundantly clear (Cf. Scriven, 1959).

If we interpret causality in the terms indicated earlier, it seems reasonable to say that integrating explanations are causal. For they can be viewed as stating either a general sufficient condition or an important necessary condition of the phenomenon to be explained. The 'cause' of homologies is the historical derivation of the organisms concerned from remote common ancestors. The historical derivation, taken as a temporal whole, is sufficient to bring about the phenomenon. Similarly, the 'cause' of vestiges is the long process of descent which connects the individuals possessing them with organisms who had fully developed, functional structures of which the vestiges are non-functional remains. The 'cause' of biogeographical distribution cannot be specified without including as an essential component the genetic descent of existing flora and fauna from ancestral types. These ways of speaking are both natural and in accord with what many biologists do actually say. Causal language fits the situation perfectly.

When the doctrine of historical derivation from a common ancestry is taken to be a sufficient condition of homologies or vestiges, the resulting explanation, though satisfactory on its own level of generality, by no means precludes a more detailed explanation at a less general level. In the latter case, the sufficient condition is shown to be internally complex and analysable into constituent parts. Instead of being taken as a temporal whole, it is resolved into a temporal succession of conditions which culminate in the phenomena to be explained. At this level there occur the 'narrative explanations' to be examined in the next section. The explanations which presently concern us perform their office by representing the phenomena concerned as the outcome of, or as partly dependent on, a historical process having continuity and direction. But no analysis of the continuity or the direction is provided. Integrating explanations can, nevertheless, be entirely adequate in their own contexts, and are compatible with other modes of explanation which particularize the events involved.

A correlative of the fact that homologies, vestiges, biogeographical distribution, etc, are explained historically in terms of the hypothesis of descent with modification, is that these phenomena constitute indirect evidence which confirms that hypothesis. Our knowledge that evolution has taken place in a specific line of descent rests primarily on fossil series that have been discovered. The general historical statement that evolution has occurred also rests primarily on the known fossil record. Yet powerful supplementary confirmation of that statement comes from the findings of comparative anatomy, physiology, embryology and biochemistry, and from the findings of biogeography, serology and even taxonomy. The diverse sources of this indirect evidence make its confirming function all the more impressive. Each of the sources is, moreover, a region in which negative evidence, if there is any, might arise. Hence the hypothesis of descent with modification is in principle falsifiable, though so far no disconfirming evidence has turned up. Nor does it seem likely that any ever will turn up.

(B) Narrative Explanations

The history of terrestrial life is known with assurance in its broadest outlines. Thus, it is certain that marine chordates existed before fishes, that fishes preceded amphibians, that amphibians preceded reptiles, and so on. But we are unable to 'read off' from the fossil record a detailed account of critical phases of this history. We know that at a certain stage of evolution vertebrates left their aquatic environment and occupied dry land. At another stage, the ancestors of men probably moved from an arboreal to a terrestrial way of life. At still other stages important lines of derivation came to an end. The sabre-tooths and the Irish elk disappeared. But by merely looking at the fossil record we cannot explain why these events took place. Some theoretical reconstruction has to be proposed of the manner of their 'coming-to-be' or 'ceasing-to-be'. Since the aim is to make these events intelligible as unique, non-recurrent phenomena, recourse must be had to historical or 'narrative' explanations. The situation does not permit of being treated systematically in terms of general laws. Hence, narrative explanations enter into evolutionary theory at points where singular events of major importance for the history of life are being discussed.

In order to discern the structure of these explanations, it will be well to look at one or two cases. Let us begin with the case which involves the first occupation of dry land by the vertebrates. This event occurred in the Devonian period, and was due to the activities of primitive amphibians which possessed rudimentary limbs and which inhabited the fresh-water pools and streams of that day. An influential explanation put forward to account for that event runs as follows:

'Why should the amphibians have developed these limbs and become potential land-dwellers? Not to breathe air, for that could be done by merely coming to the surface of the pool. Not because they were driven out in search of food, for they were fish-eating types for which there was little food to be had on land. Not to escape enemies, for they were among the largest animals of the streams and pools of that day.

'The development of limbs and the consequent ability to live on land seem, paradoxically, to have been adaptations for remaining in the water, and true land life seems to have been, so to speak, only the result of a happy accident. . . .

'The Devonian, the period in which the amphibians originated, was a time of seasonal droughts. At times the streams would cease to flow. . . . If the water dried up altogether and did not soon return . . . the amphibian, with his newly-developed land limbs, could crawl out of the shrunken pool, walk up or down the stream bed or overland and reach another pool where he might take up his aquatic existence again. Land limbs were developed to reach the water, not to leave it.

'Once this development of limbs had taken place, however, it is not hard to imagine how true land life eventually resulted. Instead of immediately taking to the water again, the amphibian might learn to linger about the drying pools and devour stranded fish. Insects were already present and would afford the beginnings of a diet for a land form. Later, plants were taken up as a source of food supply. . . . Finally, through these various developments, a land fauna would have been established' (Romer, 1941, 47-48).

This piece of reasoning has a number of interesting features. Although it is part of a scientific discussion, it is not aimed at the discovery or the confirmation of a law. It does not establish any new empirical fact which is simply to be added to the store of human knowledge. It does not make an explicit positive prediction about what will be found by future investigations, though there is a sense in which it makes certain negative predictions, as I will indicate below. What the reasoning does is to offer an explanation of a single event. It endeavours to say why the primitive amphibians should have become land-dwellers. Moreover, the explanation consists not in deducing the event from a law or set of laws, but in proposing an intelligible sequence of occurrences such that the event to be explained 'falls into place' as the terminal phase of it. The event ceases to be isolated and is connected in an orderly way with states of affairs which led up to it. Thus the explanation proposed is a historical one.

A second example of this sort of explanation can be seen in an account which has been given of why the immediate precursors of man abandoned their mode of life in the trees and became earth-dwellers. Evidence points to the conclusion that this particular event—of momentous significance for the evolution of humanity—took place somewhere in Central Asia during the Miocene or Pliocene epochs.

'The actual descent from the trees seems to have been due to a chain of events. . . . The Miocene uplift, with consequent aridity, has been mentioned. As a direct result, the stupendous barrier of the Himalayas began to arise, cutting off the forests of central Asia from their old-time continuity with those of India, and thereby severing the lines of communication by which the Anthropoids had left the cradle of their evolution. Miocene and Pliocene aridity diminished the northern forests . . . until finally there were detached wooded areas, within which the contained primates were as isolated as is the orang utan of sea-girt Borneo and Sumatra today. Further diminution of the forests compelled the descent to the ground on the part of the larger and more intelligent forms among them, and the destruction of such as could not meet terrestrial competition. Thus, a man-like, tree-borne primate became an earth-borne creature. . . . This meant the assumption of an erect posture, and the lengthening and strengthening of the lower limbs for speed, while the hands, released from the fetters of their earlier locomotive function, became the organs of the mind. Now man had to compete with the mighty carnivores, and as nature had ill-endowed him with defensive weapons, he had to devise crude armaments of stick or stone with which to ensure survival. The dwindling forests, especially as their tropical character had gone, no longer supplied an easily gained livelihood, and sustenance had to be sought from other sources' (Lull, 1929, 142).

Whether this 'chain of events' is ultimately acceptable as an explanation of the phenomenon in question does not matter for present purposes. The sole point of importance is that the explanation occurs in the context of a scientific discussion and has a clearly historical character.

The two examples just cited, like integrating explanations, can be plausibly reconstructed in causal terms. Take the line of reasoning in the first example. We can consider it as formulating by means of a pattern of statements a complex sufficient condition of the event to be explained. The components of this pattern are either statements of necessary conditions of the event (e.g. that the amphibians must have emerged from the water to become land-dwellers, that they must have found suitable food after they emerged, etc) or statements of contingent, contributory conditions (e.g. that the amphibians walked up or down stream or overland, etc). The necessary and contributory conditions which make up the complex sufficient condition are arranged in temporal sequence. But it is fairly evident that no exhaustive list of them is given. Only those which are 'crucial' or 'most important' are stated. As a matter of fact, the example in question takes for granted, and hence does not mention, two important, independently necessary conditions of the event being explained: (i) the existence of a group of fishes functionally able to move on land and genetically capable of improving this adaptation; and (ii) the accessibility of an appropriate environmental niche less hazardous to them than remaining in the water. It is essential, of course, that the temporal sequence of conditions specified by the explanation should form an intelligible, broadly continuous series. It is also essential that the component conditions be compatible with the overall sufficient condition. The latter provides a basis for deciding what the explanatory pattern may include and what it must exclude.

The causal features of the explanation can be further brought out by considering the circumstances under which it is formulated. The evolutionist is confronted with a problem, *viz*, Why did the amphibians become land-dwellers? There is a unique event, E, which he needs to explain. His first move is to propose as a solution: 'E because *s*', where *s* is a possible sufficient condition of E. The choice of *s* is made in the light of existing knowledge or reasonable inference therefrom. It may be made, as in the present example, after other possibilities have been eliminated (the amphibians did *not* become land-dwellers because they were driven out of the water by the necessity of breathing air, or of obtaining food, or of escaping from predators). These possibilities are incompatible with available scientific knowledge. The sufficient condition which is chosen (that the ability to live on land was an adaptation for continuing to live in water) is compatible with everything known. But it is formulated in such a way as to be vague, and in this case, paradoxical. To remove its paradoxical character and reduce its vagueness, a number of the component events which it embraces are related in temporal sequence. 'E because *s*' now becomes 'E because $n_1 \& n_2 \& n_3 \& c_1 \& c_2 \& n_4 \ldots$ etc', where *n* and *c* stand for necessary and contributory conditions respectively. The sequence constructed is, of course, no more than a *possible* explanation at this stage; and it is worth noting how much use is made throughout of the possibility-expressing auxiliaries, 'could', 'would', and 'might'. They indicate the conjectural nature of many of the conditions postulated by the pattern.

It may be tempting to try to make this pattern conform to certain familiar 'models' of explanation. The first is the model of a hierarchical deductive system, often declared to be the ideal form in which the theoretical part of every science ought to be cast, or, at any rate, to which the theoretical part ought to approximate. The attraction exerted by this model is mainly due to its successful use in connection with physics. But it does not seem to be applicable to patterns of historical explanation in biology. Certainly, the temporal sequence of events specified by the above example is not such as to permit each event to be deductively inferred from its predecessors. The presence of many contingent, contributory conditions in the sequence makes it idle to hope that the statements constituting the explanatory pattern can be organized deductively, or even, perhaps, axiomatically. The deductive model is, therefore, the wrong one to have in mind at this point, however relevant it may be elsewhere.

A second model (or analogy) which we may try to use is that of a 'causal chain'. We may be inclined to say of the example under consideration that the temporally successive events depicted form a chain, each 'link' of which is the effect of its immediate predecessor and the cause of its immediate successor. The initial link is simply an event whose predecessor we disregard; and the concluding link, being the event we wish to explain, is one whose successor we disregard. Now there may be some appropriateness in employing the metaphorical expression, 'chain of events', as the author of the second example does, to represent what the explanatory pattern depicts. But it is scarcely satisfactory to start thinking of it as a *causal* chain. For one thing, this analogy tends to obscure the fact that each component of the pattern is specified in accordance with an accepted background of knowledge, or more specifically, an accepted background of assumptions, theories, information, etc. Each component belongs to a context and is not an isolated, atomic 'link'. Furthermore, the analogy falsely suggests that the specification of the components is exhaustive. One cannot have a 'chain' if links are missing. In short, the causal chain model tempts us to overlook the importance of contextual consideration here, as elsewhere (Cf. Hanson, 1955). An explanatory pattern of the sort we are examining is not so much a segment of a separate causal line stretching back into the past, as it is a portion of an intricate network having an enormous number of cross-connections.

The most illuminating parallel, however, is with a mode of explanation often adopted by historians. In order to explain what took place at a particular juncture of human affairs, they produce a coherent narrative of the events concerned. This may involve reconstructing certain of the events, selecting those which vitally affected or foreshadowed later developments, arranging the events in a significant order, etc, so as to tell a 'likely story'. The aim is to make the sequence of events intelligible as a relatively independent whole. In a similar way the explanatory pattern we are considering forms a coherent or connected narrative which represents a number of possible events in an intelligible sequence. Hence the pattern is appropriately called a 'narrative explanation'.

It is evident that narrative explanations are constructed without mentioning any general laws. Like integrating explanations, they provide no basis for precise positive predictions. In both cases, nevertheless, there is a background of general information, which includes much that rests on rough inductive grounds. The background may be regarded as a set of 'boundary conditions' in accordance with which the explanations are formulated. Take the two examples presented above. In the case of the first, although the explanation of the origin of land fauna presupposes the origin of vertebrates, we do not have to explain the latter in order to explain the former. We can accept the explanation given, treating it as a self-contained pattern whose limits do not need to be explicitly formulated. Whatever force the explanation has is independent of them. The same is true of the account of why man's immediate precursors became land-borne creatures. No reasonable person would refuse to accept this account simply because it fails to include an account of why these precursors themselves became tree-dwellers. The alternative to admitting boundary or background conditions for a given explanation is to insist that we must always seek 'ultimate' explanations which have no such boundaries. A very slight logical pressure is sufficient to transform this into the doctrine that we must 'explain the total universe' before we can 'really' explain any part or aspect of it. But this doctrine empties the idea of explanation of both its scientific and its commonsense meaning. Hence, for present purposes the doctrine may be disregarded.

The boundary or background conditions of a particular narrative explanation undoubtedly contain a vast array of prior information, assumptions, inductive generalizations, etc. This array is, however, not peculiar to that explanation, but forms a body of general knowledge from which many different inquiries must start. If laws are involved, they are so trivial 'that we need not mention them and rarely even notice them' (Popper, 1957b, 145). They are, therefore, extrinsic to the structure of the narrative explanation itself. Yet each component of the latter must be such as not to conflict in any way with the background conditions. Hence they are by no means irrelevant to the explanation's structure. Nevertheless, there is a fundamental contrast here with the standard form of systematic explanation whose structure does embody laws or general statements. Good reasons exist, then, for contending that narrative explanations 'explain' in a manner unlike that of systematic explanations, though both types are essentially causal.

To conclude this part of the discussion, I will take up two objections which might be raised against it. 'You have contended,' a critic may say, 'that a narrative explanation in evolutionary theory specifies a possible sufficient condition of an individual or singular event; and that in order to make the explanation fit the event with precision, a number of component conditions (necessary and contributory) are narrated in temporal sequence. You have further contended that the explanatory force of the resulting pattern of statements resides not in any general laws which it involves, but rather in the extent to which it establishes an intelligible, broadly continuous series of occurrences which leads up to the event in question. But surely if a genuine sufficient condition, s, of the event, E, is established, we *can* formulate a law, viz., "Whenever there is a condition of the kind s, there will be an event of the kind E." Hence, contrary to what you say, the explanatory pattern is really deductive in form. It has this law as a major premiss, a statement specifying s as a minor premiss, and a statement specifying E as the conclusion. Moreover, the presence of the law gives the pattern a predictive power exactly like that of any other scientific theory. Accordingly, the difference you have alleged between narrative and systematic explanations is chimerical. No ground whatsoever exists for supposing that evolutionary theory contains two dissimilar modes of explaining the phenomena with which it deals.'

The reply to this objection is, I think, as follows. Whenever a narrative explanation of an event in evolution is called for, the event is not an instance of a kind, but is a singular occurrence, something which has happened just once and which cannot recur. It is, therefore, not material for any generalization or law. The same is true of its proposed explanation. What we seek to formulate is a temporal sequence of conditions which, taken as a whole, constitutes a unique sufficient condition of *that* event. This sequence will likewise never recur, though various elements of it may. When, therefore, we affirm 'E because s', under the above circumstances, we are not committed to the empirical generalization (or law) 'Whenever s, then E'. What we are committed to, of course, is the *logical principle* 'If s, then E', for its acceptance is required in order to argue 'E because s'. But the logical principle does not function as a premiss in an argument; the affirmation, 'E because s', is not deducible from it (Cf. Ryle, 1950). Both s and E are concrete, individual phenomena between which an individual relation holds.

A critic may, however, urge another objection. 'According to your analysis,' he may contend, 'a narrative explanation in evolutionary theory is a pattern of statements devoid of any generalizations or laws. The pattern, therefore, does not, and cannot, allow any predictions to be made. If so, there is no way in which it can be empirically tested. We can ensure that it is internally coherent, that its components form a broadly continuous sequence, and that each of them is in accord with available scientific knowledge. Yet because no predictions are implied, we can never subject the proposed explanation to any verificational procedures. In that case it remains a sheer conjecture about a past event. Surely you do not suggest that this kind of thing belongs to a scientific theory?'

The appropriate reply here, it seems to me, consists in drawing a distinction between positive and negative predictions. It is true that a historical explanation of the sort we have been discussing does not allow any positive predictions to be made. But in as much as the explanation does specify a determinate temporal sequence of events, it restricts the possibilities with regard to what future investigations will disclose. The pattern does, therefore, involve a number of negative predictions. It implies that certain phenomena *will not turn up* in any future empirical inquiries (e.g. in paleontology, comparative anatomy, experimental biology, etc). If one of these phenomena does turn up it will invalidate or falsify the pattern. Hence, narrative explanations in evolutionary theory *are* empirically testable, for nothing prevents their inadequacy from being detected, in the long run, if they are inadequate (Cf. Hayek, 1955). Since, as we have previously mentioned, a distinguishing mark of a scientific theory is its falsifiability, i.e. the possibility of overthrowing it on the basis of empirical evidence, these historical explanations can be regarded as respectable constituents of evolutionary science.

This consideration allows us to formulate a rule of selection for use in situations where more than one explanatory pattern relevant to a given event, E, can be devised. Suppose that s_1 and s_2 are a pair of possible sufficient conditions of E; and that in the case of s_2 we are able to specify a smaller number of the component conditions (necessary and contributory) than in the case of s_1. It follows that s_1 will then be more readily shown to be inadequate than s_2. In other words, s_1 is a more testable pattern than

s_2 because the temporal sequence of conditions presented in the case of the former involves a larger number of negative predictions than does the temporal sequence presented by the latter. This fact should lead us to choose s_1 rather than s_2 as an explanation of E. The same considerations will apply where more than two possibilities are available as sufficient conditions. Although an explanatory pattern is always falsifiable if properly constructed, I believe that Popper is correct in insisting that no pattern can ever be conclusively verified. It may, nevertheless, be *progressively* verified as the result of a long series of unsuccessful attempts to overthrow it. At bottom, then, each explanatory pattern is an *informed conjecture* about the origin or the termination of a past event—not a categorical affirmation of the truth, but an attempt to find out the truth about it (Cf. Popper, 1956; 1957a).

Since the making of exaggerated claims is an occupational ailment of philosophers, I can perhaps avoid it here by a concluding statement. I believe the discussion has shown that evolutionary theory does contain historical explanations, that some of them are plausibly reconstructed in causal terms, and that the reconstruction does not involve bringing a single event under a general law. That *all* historical explanations are causal and that *none* of them use laws has not been shown. Unless one set up a theoretical Procrustean bed, I fail to see how these things could be shown. At any rate, nothing of the sort has been undertaken in the present section.

3. SYSTEMATIC EXPLANATIONS IN EVOLUTIONARY THEORY

Historical explanations, I have been arguing, form an essential part of evolutionary theory. Without them it would be impossible to account for many features of present-day organisms, and for many non-recurrent episodes in phylogenesis. Yet there are clearly a number of recurrent phenomena in evolution—the manifold adaptations of living things to their environmental niches, phylogenetic trends, the formation of species, the occurrence of extinction, etc—which cannot be explained historically. Furthermore, the total course of evolution, together with all its large-scale features, has to be explained. If this is to be done, reference must be made to factors presumed to have been operative during all or most of the history of life. These factors will have to be set forth in an explanatory pattern which contains general statements or laws. The pattern will therefore be more abstract in content than is the case with historical explanations. My main concern will be to report the gist of what modern selectionist theory has to say on this subject. But as an introduction, I will make some remarks about other doctrines—vitalism, finalism and Neo-lamarckism—which have sometimes sought to compete with selectionism. I will consider the doctrines here as competitors for the rôle of a *scientific* explanation of evolution, and will treat them only in outline.

(A) Vitalism, Finalism and Neo-lamarckism

A theory may be described as 'vitalistic' if it purports to give a systematic explanation of evolution in terms of some unique, non-natural agency. This agency, which has been called by various names—the 'life force', 'elan vital', 'entelechy', etc, is affirmed to be a necessary condition, or the necessary and sufficient condition, of the evolutionary process. The uniqueness of the agency is due to its not being describable in terms which apply to anything else. Strictly speaking, it can only be named. It is non-natural in the sense that while its effects occur in the spatio-temporal world, the agency itself lies 'outside' or 'beyond' that world. Hence, it cannot be disclosed to empirical observation, no matter how refined. Nevertheless, without it, the evolution of living things would have failed to occur. Those who advocate this view may or may not regard the minute details of the evolutionary process as effects of the vital agency. But the large-scale aspects of the process are regarded as such effects. Thus the fact that evolution has been incremental, complicating, differentiating, productive of increased efficiency, opportunistic, etc, is attributed to the vital agency and is held to constitute evidence of its 'driving power'. To identify this factor is to locate the ultimate cause of phylogenesis.

It is not essential that a vitalistic doctrine should also be teleological or 'finalistic', though it usually is so. The vital agency can be conceived as an unconscious force which neither realizes any purposes in the successive effects it produces nor works towards an ultimate goal. On this approach, the course of evolution is the wholly unplanned outcome of the unconscious force, which remains forever inscrutable and mysterious. In general, however, vitalistic theories make the opposite assumption, namely that the course of evolution illustrates the manner in which the vital agency moves towards a final goal. That is to say, vitalism and finalism are combined. The goal of evolution may be represented in a variety of ways as the maximizing of life, the production of man, the realizing of absolute freedom, etc. Since the achieving of the goal is implicit in the evolutionary process, it may be argued that the vital agency must be allowed some degree of foresight and hence of consciousness. From this point many extrapolations can be made which lead into the domain of natural theology.

Just as vitalism is not necessarily finalistic, so finalism is not necessarily vitalistic. For the core of finalism is the contention that a necessary condition of evolution consists of its orientation towards an ultimate goal. This orientation is a 'final cause' in the classical sense, but it may be combined with a number of 'efficient causes' which are non-vitalistic. We are perfectly familiar with mechanically determined processes oriented towards fixed ends or goals. The operations of man-made machines provide the most obvious examples—self-propelled, target-seeking missiles, automatic steering systems, etc, being cases in point. Here, of course, the final cause is the result of the planning activities of human beings who have set up the mechanical conditions which make the operations possible. Goal-seeking machines or 'teleological mechanisms', as they are sometimes called, require the intelligence of men to bring them into being. Similarly, a finalism which posited only mechanistic factors among its efficient causes might be held to imply the operation of a transcendent 'designer' or 'planner', and hence would again open a path to natural theology. If such a conception is deemed inadequate, then recourse will almost certainly be had to a combination of vitalism and finalism (Cf. Raven, 1953).

Hostile critics have sometimes said that all these doctrines are untenable because their central concepts are incapable of being correlated with what can be observed. The concepts are, therefore, devoid of scientific meaning. Biologists have never perceived, and will never perceive, a 'vital force' or 'entelechy'. This alleged factor which is supposed to be present in all living things and to determine the course of evolution cannot be displayed to view. Likewise, biologists have never perceived, and will never perceive, the 'final end' or 'ultimate goal' towards which evolution is sup-

F

posed to be moving. These concepts are fictions, the products of wishful and anthropomorphic thinking. They can have no place in a scientific theory of evolution.

The preceding sentence states a conclusion with which I concur. But I think that the critics have given an inadequate reason for holding it. In the light of the history of science it is not legitimate to reject such notions as a 'vital force', 'entelechy', etc, merely because they lack perceptual correlates. For as we have mentioned, the abstract concepts which belong to established scientific theories also have this feature. Yet although these abstract concepts have no empirical interpretation, they do have systematic or deductive connections with concepts occurring in observation-statements entailed by the theories. It is precisely here that vitalism and finalism are vulnerable. One cannot find in them any indication of how the notions of a 'vital force' or an 'ultimate evolutionary goal' are systematically linked with other concepts having a direct reference to experiential data. Hence there is no way by which empirical meaning can be indirectly conferred on the notions, as is the case with the 'theoretical constructs' belonging to established scientific theories. One consequence of the logical isolation of their central notions is that neither vitalism nor finalism is capable of being falsified by empirical evidence. This seems to me the basic reason for refusing to admit them to the ranks of scientific explanations of evolution.

What has been said does not imply that vitalists and finalists refrain from appealing to empirical evidence in support of their doctrines. On the contrary, two such influential vitalists as Bergson and Driesch frequently cite observed 'facts' which are held to be explicable only on vitalistic premises. But the trouble here is that the authenticity of some of these 'facts' has been challenged by competent investigators; while the facts that are uncontroversial can be brought, at least in principle, within the scope of non-vitalistic theories (Cf. Haldane, 1932a; Bertalanffy, 1952). It is perfectly true that Driesch was not primarily concerned with discovering the causes of evolution but with deriving metaphysical conclusions from his experimental study of embryological processes (Driesch, 1908). Similarly, Bergson was concerned to express a quasi-poetic vision of evolution, not to give a scientific account of it (Bergson, 1911). Nonetheless, the impression has been created that these two vitalists, by introducing empirical considerations into their work, are doing the same kind of thing as a biologist who appeals to evidence in support of a scientific hypothesis. That this is not so seems obvious. Lesser versions of vitalism and finalism, of which there are an indefinite number, are even more vulnerable to the aforementioned criticism.

Another doctrine which falls into this general category is the causal interpretation of orthogenesis. It seeks to account not for the total evolutionary process but for the long-term trends which paleontologists describe. These trends are supposed to be caused by a special, orthogenetic 'principle' whose action results in their being continued in one direction for millions of years, quite independently of environmental circumstances. The principle may be held to be an 'inner urge' which is part of the constitution of the organisms involved in the trend; or it may be held to direct their changes *ab extra* in some non-natural fashion. The principle may be interpreted monistically as an indivisible unity, or pluralistically as a factor present in a multiplicity of organic centres. It is nearly always affirmed to have a goal, which may be specific to each trend or the same for all trends. These are just a few of the variations that have been worked on the orthogenetic theme (Cf. Jepsen, 1949).

Now in so far as this special principle is supposed to act on certain populations from without, so as to cause them to evolve in one direction for long periods, there is little to differentiate orthogenesis from vitalism and finalism. It is therefore open to the same objections which tell against them. Not all versions of the doctrine, of course, take this form. Berg (1926), for example, has argued that most evolutionary sequences are the result of certain processes inherent in organisms. But these processes are purely physical, or physico-chemical, and conform to universal laws. Here no mysterious vital force or entelechy is postulated. Yet the orienting processes, because they are vaguely specified, seem as inaccessible to empirical investigation as the factors appealed to by vitalism and finalism. The 'universal laws' which are alleged to govern the processes remain equally obscure, despite Berg's powerful presentation of the case.

With the rise of the modern selectionist theory of evolution, interest in orthogenesis has diminished. It is now clear that few really 'straight-line' trends are indicated by the paleontological data. Most trends exhibit irregularities, branching, and changes of direction. Even where ostensibly rectilinear sequences occur,

they may be accounted for without having recourse to an orthogenetic principle. 'Phyletic lines of this sort are reasonably to
be considered as due to orthoselection, a process of increasingly
improved adaptation to a relatively stable environment. Under
such conditions, any deviation from the "normal" line would
be negative as to survival-value and would tend to be eliminated;
the potential branches of the "tree" would tend to be pruned
by selection before they became marked enough to be apparent
in the fossil record' (Romer, 1949, 107). In such cases, orthoselection is a more fruitful hypothesis than orthogenesis.

The retort may be made that orthoselection can scarcely yield
a plausible explanation of the precise parallelism observed in
trends belonging to quite distinct or even unrelated phyletic
lines. And it cannot explain at all trends which involve non-
adaptive or inadaptive traits. How can orthoselection possibly
explain the development of the gigantic antlers whose cumber-
someness must have accelerated the extinction of the Irish elk?
What 'improved adaptation' can there have been in the trend
which produced the monstrous canines of the now extinct
sabretooths? In these and other instances evolution seems to
have had an inner 'momentum' which led to the overdevelop-
ment of certain organs, carrying them far beyond the point of
optimum value so that they became positively disadvantageous
to their possessors. And if these trends had an inner momentum,
why may not the same be true of all trends? To answer affirmatively is tantamount to admitting the presence of an orthogenetic
factor in evolution; and there are substantial reasons for giving
such an answer.

Exponents of modern selectionism have not found it impossible
to propose explanations of these phenomena (Cf. Simpson, 1944,
1949; Carter, 1951). But the issues involved are of too technical
a nature to be treated here. Anyone who asserted that orthoselection can account for *all* known paleontological trends would
be making an unjustified claim. For in this domain there are still
a great many unsolved problems. And it is sounder to admit
that they are unsolved, rather than to seek an explanation in so
vaguely formulated a principle as that of orthogenesis.

A more formidable theory of evolutionary causality, regarded
by many as the only serious alternative to Darwin's, is Neo-
lamarckism. According to it, the course of evolution is due to
the following factors: (i) a changing environment which acts

on individual organisms; (ii) the consequent production of new needs in those organisms, needs which must be met if the organisms are to survive; (iii) the active response of some organisms to meet the needs, i.e. the establishing of new habits (or the cessation of old habits) of use of various bodily parts; (iv) a resulting change in those parts and hence in the somatic structure of the individual organisms which possess them; and (v) the transmission of the structural changes and habits from one generation to the next, so that the organisms concerned are gradually transformed into new species. Some Neo-lamarckians add to the above the contention that the outer environment may produce effects directly upon the individual, which are then inherited by its offspring—a contention which Lamarck himself rejected. Thus the theory involves the assumption that the effects of use and disuse, or environmentally induced effects on the individual, are inherited in kind and become germinally fixed. This assumption has come to be known as 'the inheritance of acquired characteristics', a phrase by no means free from obscurity. An important consequence of Neo-lamarckism is that no 'chance' or 'random' elements enter into the course of evolution. Every one of the changes which has arisen in phylogeny came about through the action of specific causes, and in that sense the course of evolution has been strictly determined.

In support of this theory, Neo-lamarckians have usually appealed to 'evidence' of two sorts. The first sort consists of a number of 'causal reconstructions' of episodes in evolutionary history. Among these are the familiar examples of the lengthening of the neck of the giraffe as a result of ancestral members of the species reaching for the foliage of tall trees; or the production of the splay-foot of the camel as a result of its ancestors continuing to walk on yielding sand; or the gradual loss of sight in moles as a result of successive generations living underground and ceasing to use their eyes. The second sort of 'evidence' is obtained from certain experimental researches which are alleged to prove beyond reasonable doubt that the effects of use and disuse are inheritable. It is not contended that these researches establish the Neo-lamarckians' whole case. In order to do this experimentally, very complicated and difficult investigations would be necessary (Cf. MacBride, 1932). Nevertheless, so the argument runs, once laboratory studies have shown that the effects of use and disuse, together with other environmentally induced changes, *can* become fixed in the hereditary equipment of species, a major objection to Neo-lamarckism disappears. The general theory can then be rendered probable by introducing 'indirect evidence' of the first sort.

Unfortunately for the theory, it is precisely these experimental researches which are judged to be unsatisfactory by non-Lamarckian biologists. Both the method employed in conducting the experiments and the results obtained have been widely questioned (Cf. Haldane, 1932b; Huxley, 1942). The experiments yield no evidence which compels the assent of qualified inquirers. A layman can only conclude that 'Lamarckian inheritance' has not been proved to occur in the cases cited. Furthermore, geneticists have been unable to locate any mechanism by which changes in the habits or the bodily structure of individual organisms could affect their reproductive cells in such a way as to become part of the hereditary equipment of subsequent generations. Until such a mechanism is discovered, or at any rate until there is a verifiable theory of how 'the inheritance of acquired characteristics' is effected, Neo-lamarckism remains a doctrine with a grave weakness in its very formulation.

Even if the above deficiencies were corrected, the doctrine would encounter other difficulties. Chief among these are (i) the existence of non-adaptive changes in individuals belonging to small populations; (ii) adaptive changes which have occurred in neuter insects; and (iii) many cases of protective coloration and mimicry. Such facts seem *prima facie* to constitute negative evidence which Neo-lamarckism is not in a position to handle. It is always possible, of course, that the theory could be reformulated so as to escape from these difficulties. But just how this might be done is by no means obvious.

The upshot of the matter may be summarized as follows. From a methodological standpoint, Neo-lamarckism is an explanatory theory of evolution vastly superior to both vitalism and finalism. Its conceptual structure contains no elements which are in principle beyond the range of empirical investigations. The theory is thus testable. Yet available tests, while they do not conclusively falsify it, render the theory suspect. Experiments alleged to provide it with support by showing that Lamarckian inheritance does take place are controversial and inconclusive. Finally, the idea of such inheritance appears incompatible with the body of knowledge so far assembled by the science of genetics. There is no known mechanism by which acquired characters could be transmitted, and little prospect of finding one. It is, then, hardly surprising that while Neo-lamarckism still has a few vigorous defenders among biologists (Cf. Lindsey, 1952; Martin, 1957; Cannon, 1958), no wide support for this position has been achieved. It seems clear that we have to look elsewhere for a more satisfactory account of the causes of evolution.

(B) *Modern Selectionist Theory*

The opening paragraphs of this study referred to the rapid developments in evolutionary theory which have taken place during the last few decades. A central feature of these developments has been the extension of the Darwinian doctrine of natural selection and the synthesis of it with the basic principles of genetics. The result has been called 'the synthetic theory' of evolutionary causality (Simpson, 1949), 'modern selectionist theory', or simply 'reborn Darwinism' (Huxley, 1942). A majority of biologists regard this as the most adequate explanatory account of evolution so far advanced. We will next consider the main ingredients of the theory, beginning with the genetic factors.

(i) *Genetic factors in evolution.* The evolution of a population is a historical process marked by two sorts of changes in the individual organisms concerned. There are changes which take place in the observable form and functions of individuals belonging to successive generations of a population (changes of phenotype); and there are changes which take place in the genetic constitution of these individuals (changes of genotype). The only phenotypic changes which are of evolutionary significance are those causally determined by alterations of the genotype, for otherwise the phenotypic changes will not be transmitted from one generation to the next. It follows that genotypic changes are a necessary condition of evolution. Without them, the members of each generation of a population might differ slightly in their observable features from the members of the preceding generation, but these differences would be due to the environment alone, and because they were non-inheritable, could not lead to cumulative changes extending over a number of generations of the population. A review of certain important things known or conjectured about genotypic changes will therefore be in order.

An individual genotype is an integrated system of discrete units (genes and chromosomes) which has a high degree of stability. Its stability is due primarily to the remarkable power of the units to produce exact copies of themselves. This is referred to as the power of 'self-copying' ('self-reproduction', 'autosynthesis', etc), and it is a distinctive feature of living substances. Because of it, genetic units transmit copies of themselves from one generation of a population to the next. Another way of putting this is to say that the units are vehicles for conveying 'information' about certain aspects of the life of past organisms. Each copy of a unit is a kind of 'inherited message' received by offspring from their ancestors; and because organisms utilize the information thus conveyed, successive generations tend to keep within the limits of a stable, common pattern (Cf. Young, 1957). A certain number of genotypic changes do occur through the shuffling or recombination of the units in sexual reproduction or through the process of hybridization. Such changes, however, since they do not involve any alteration of the units themselves, seem to be of relatively minor importance in evolution. Yet they cannot be ignored without over-simplifying the total picture.

If the stability of the genotype were not counterbalanced by a capacity to alter, evolution would be impossible. This capacity is manifested as the phenomenon of 'mutation', an event which occurs at infrequent intervals in genetic units. Because of this event, new phenotypic characters arise in members of a population and, provided certain conditions are fulfilled, are subsequently manifested by their descendants. No understanding of evolutionary causality can be gained without appreciating the rôle played by mutations in the history of living things.

Sometimes the word 'mutation' is used to refer to a type of change which happens to both chromosomes and genes. Yet it is desirable to distinguish the two cases. For genes (at any rate, nuclear genes) are self-copying units *within* chromosomes. Any destruction, multiplication, or spatial rearrangement of these units is thought to cause a chromosomal change, and this can be called an 'aberration' to distinguish it from a 'mutation' proper (Dobzhansky, 1951). The latter term can then be restricted to the more basic process by which changes occur in genes. Such changes result in alterations of the corresponding genotype, and so produce new phenotypic traits. Fresh ingredients are thereby injected into the evolutionary stream. Thus it has often been said that gene mutations provide 'the raw material of evolution' (Huxley, 1942, 115; 1953, 41; Dobzhansky, 1950b, 210).

Mutations are not directly observed events. They are inferred causes of observed phenotypic changes. Now since these changes may be large or small, a corresponding variation in size is assumed to exist on the part of their causes. Accordingly, provision is made for admitting *macro-mutations*, whose effects are large, and *micro-mutations*, whose effects are small (Carter, 1951). Because a genotype is an integrated system, changes within it are more likely than not to be disruptive. It is therefore agreed that the vast majority of mutations, especially large ones, are harmful —in most cases, lethal—to the organisms in which they occur. Small mutations, the sort which we have reason to believe occur with the greatest frequency in wild populations, may prove beneficial to their carriers. Hence small mutations are considered to provide the main material used by evolution.

Discussions of this topic with which I am acquainted do not make entirely clear the logic of the word 'mutation'. Consider the locution: 'In a certain population, gene X mutated.' What is said here exhibits two ambiguities. (*a*) No account is taken of the distinction between gene X as a *type* and the particular copies or *instances* of it. (*b*) It is not made clear whether a mutation is a change of an effective property of a gene, so that *one and the same* gene can undergo successive mutations by changing successively its effective properties; or whether a mutation is a change by which an existing gene becomes a *different* gene with different properties. Accordingly, the locution, 'In a certain population, gene X mutated,' might be understood to mean either (i) 'a single instance, several instances, or all instances of gene X altered at least one effective property'; or (ii) 'a single instance, several instances, or all instances of gene X became gene Y'.

These are not trivial distinctions. They have an important bearing on what can be said, for example, about the question: Have mutations produced any new genes since the beginning of life on the earth? If the situation specified in (ii) has *never* occurred, the answer to the question is 'No'. The same set of genes exists now as existed when life began, although enormous changes in their effective properties must have taken place. If the situation specified in (ii) has *sometimes* occurred, the answer to the question is 'Yes'. Again, suppose we wonder whether mutations have *added* new genes to the total supply in the living world. We should have to come to a negative conclusion if it is the case that whenever a gene X mutates *all* its instances become gene Y. For then gene X disappears from the living world, and gene Y replaces it. If, therefore, the present supply of types of genes in the world contains some of the original types together with a number of new types, then either the original types have not undergone mutation, or the sort of change specified in (i) above has happened to them. It hardly needs to be said that no factual questions can be settled by making these distinctions. But the failure to make them may lead to the overlooking of factual questions which merit investigation.

Returning to the conclusions of current genetic theory, we may note that no evidence has been found to support the view that mutations can be caused by the needs or requirements of individual organisms. Organisms lack the capacity to produce beneficial mutations when and where the latter are required to ensure viability. The adaptive exigencies of living things are not to be included among the necessary and sufficient conditions of any mutation.

This conclusion is of special significance for modern selectionist theory. Yet the conclusion is sometimes stated in language which may create a false impression. Thus it is said that mutations are 'accidental' or 'fortuitous', and this might be understood to mean that they lack causes. There is, however, no warrant for such a view. On the contrary, ever since 1928 geneticists have known that gene mutations can be caused by various agencies, such as X-rays, ultraviolet vays, chemicals, high temperatures, etc, to which populations of organisms are artificially subjected. These 'mutagenic' agencies are in all probability sufficient but not necessary conditions of the changes in question. Even this may be an inaccurate way of putting it, since it appears that mutagenic agencies are not specific in their mode of operation. They do not allow the exact prediction of the effects they bring about. It is true, of course, that the great bulk of mutations which occur in wild populations do not have *known* causes. But the presumption is that the causes are unknown rather than non-existent. Hence the words 'accidental' and 'fortuitous', if used at all, should be understood to signify only the present inability of geneticists to explain why each mutation takes place exactly when and where it does.

Two other adjectives often applied to mutations are 'spontaneous' and 'random'. If the former is taken to mean 'not elicited by factors external to the organism', then it does appear to be appropriately used save on those occasions when mutagenic agencies are operative. The unknown causes of the majority of mutations are conjectured to lie within the gene. It is estimated to be an entity whose size is of the molecular order and which in all probability is a giant molecule with an extremely complex structure. If so, it may be that a mutation is the result of an alteration of this structure, akin to the 'isomeric changes' that are well known in ordinary chemistry (Cf. Schrödinger, 1945). But all such suppositions are guesses. At the present time we simply do not know what it is that causes a gene to mutate spontaneously; nor, indeed, do we yet fully understand its power of self-copying. Until such time as scientific inquiry can throw more light on these matters, it will be difficult to decide with what propriety mutations are to be characterized as 'random'. If the adjective is understood to mean 'occurring in a disorderly manner in all possible directions', then there is some presumption against using it in that sense. For it is likely that the internal structure of the gene imposes limitations on the number of directions in which changes can occur. The available possibilities are almost certainly restricted. Accordingly, by 'random mutations' we can at best convey the idea that more than one direction of change is available to each gene at each moment in its history, but that the possibilities are far from unlimited.

The remark has sometimes been made (Cf. Huxley, 1953), that mutations arise from 'imperfections' in the process of self-copying. Despite the fact that self-copying is fundamental to all living matter, it occasionally fails to take place in the standard manner. On such occasions, a gene will produce not an exact copy of itself but a variant whose phenotypic effects will be 'new'. It has even been suggested that the 'failure' of the self-copying process must be attributed to a defect in the internal chemistry of the gene, so that 'the cause of mutations may be seen not in the power but in the frailty of matter' (Stern, 1953, 194). This view has curious implications. In the first place, since mutations are a necessary condition of evolution, the view implies that evolution would not have occurred if organic matter had always behaved in standard ways, and never deviated from exactitude. That is to say, if organic matter at the level of the gene had possessed an absolutely unvarying power of self-copying there would have been no evolutionary process at all. It has been to the 'imperfections' in this power that life owes its continuance. For if the first living things (e.g., protogenes) had *only* been able to duplicate themselves exactly, the population they formed would not have been able to survive when the environment became unfavourable. One wonders, therefore, how appropriate the use of such words as 'imperfection' or 'failure' is in this context. May it not be better to say that living substance has two fundamental but opposite modes of perpetuating itself, one which maintains identity through exact copying, and one which generates diversity through mutation? Both modes can then be considered necessary for evolution.

Before leaving this topic it will be well to take note of certain objections which have been made to genetic concepts and to their use in selectionist theory.

The most radical objection is directed against the concept of the gene. Genes, it has been contended, are wholly mythical entities. There is no observational evidence that they exist; and to postulate their existence is to base the science of heredity on an imaginary foundation. This objection has been vehemently urged by such opponents of genetics as Lysenko in the USSR. Since his opposition has been motivated by ideological rather than scientific considerations, it does not require discussion here. On a different plane is the opposition of the geneticist Gold-schmidt, who argues against the concept of the gene as a discrete, independently functioning particle. In his view, the basic hereditary factors are chromosomes with their complex, internal architecture. Differences can indeed be discerned and localized at various points in the architecture; and if we wish to use the expression 'gene' as a name for these localized differences, we may do so. But the expression should not be taken to name a separate entity akin to the elementary particles of physics.

Several replies to this objection have been advanced. Some have argued that the term 'gene' can be defined operationally by connecting it with experimentally determined or determinable properties. No assumptions or inferences about its existential status need be introduced. 'Operationally, the gene can be defined as the smallest segment of the gene string that can be shown to be consistently associated with occurrence of a specific genetic effect' (Stadler, 1954, 814). Others have declared that genes have now been made visible by means of the electron microscope, so that there can no longer be any doubt about their actual existence (Huxley, 1949; Sinnott, 1950). Few would nowadays defend the doctrine that genes are independent of one another in their functioning. On the contrary, it is widely recognized that they interact with one another to determine their effects, and that within a given chromosome the genes 'must be delicately adjusted to each other so as to produce a harmoniously functioning whole' (Huxley, 1942, 85). The total set of genes—and it now appears that there are cytoplasmic as well as nuclear genes (Cf. Sonneborn, 1951)—is regarded as a gene-complex, the components of which rarely, if ever, act independently of each other. These components, however, are particulate and have an intrinsic character of their own which cannot be disregarded.

Another objection to genetic concepts is directed against the doctrine of mutations. Mutations, it is argued, are by definition discontinuous changes in the hereditary material. Since the genotype is a delicately balanced system, a mutation will be a disruptive occurrence whose effects on the organism are certain to be deleterious. Hence all such occurrences will militate against an organism's success in surviving and producing offspring. Indeed, the vast majority of mutations are definitely known to be lethal. How can they possibly contribute to the evolutionary process? (Cf. Martin, 1953).

One reply to this objection stresses the distinction between a mutation and its phenotypic effects. A mutation is *per se* a discontinuous change in the genotype. But it does not necessarily produce a visible discontinuiuty in any phenotypic character. That is to say, the effects of a mutation may be slight, so that the variation involved may blend with pre-existing characters. In such cases no deleterious results will follow. On the contrary, the slight variation in the character or characters may prove definitely advantageous to the organisms in which they occur. Their ability to survive and reproduce will be enhanced. In this way mutations can contribute to evolutionary change. One of the important conclusions established by the statistical analyses previously mentioned is that even a very small margin of advantage provided by a variation in a character is enough to allow it to spread through a population in successive generations. Thus Fisher (1930) showed that a mutation which gives its possessor a 1 per cent advantage over other individuals of the same species and which has only one chance in fifty of establishing itself, can sweep through the whole species in 250 generations and might do so in ten generations. The rate of spreading of characters with different margins of advantage in populations of different sizes has been worked out by Fisher, Haldane, and Wright, and formulated in mathematical terms. Their conclusions constitute powerful indirect support for the view that mutations are a necessary condition of the evolutionary process.

Several other matters may be mentioned in bringing this section to a close.

Considerable discussion has taken place among biologists as to whether macro-mutations play any part in evolution. Although the outcome of the discussion is inconclusive, the following opinion seems to have substantial support. If by macro-mutations is meant those which are quantitatively but not qualitatively different from micro-mutations, then it is possible that they *do* function in rare instances as causal determinants of evolution. At any rate, no evidence has been adduced to show that they can *never* so function. On the other hand, if by macro-mutations is meant genetic changes different in kind rather than degree from micro-mutations, then the conception is a controversial one. The chief protagonist of the latter conception, Goldschmidt (1940), has argued with great force that large, 'systemic' mutations, involving a radical reorganization of intra-chromosomal pattern, are required to explain the occurrence in evolution of the higher categories of organisms (phyla, classes, etc). But his position has not been widely accepted (Cf., however, Wright, 1956). Opponents have objected that 'systemic' mutations are too unlike anything which has ever been observed to be scientifically admissible. Furthermore, the phenomena they purport to explain can probably be accounted for on other, less dubious grounds. This whole controversy, however, is far from settled, and must appear to a layman as still *sub judice*.

There can be no doubt that the concepts and principles of genetics have contributed greatly to the formulation of an adequate theory of evolution. Yet it should not be forgotten that when these concepts and principles are declared to apply to *all* organisms, past and present, an enormous extrapolation is being made. Actually, geneticists have investigated empirically only a minute fraction of living things. Mayr remarked in 1942, that 'up to the present time only about one five-hundredth of one per cent of the known species of animals have been studied with any degree of thoroughness by geneticists' (Mayr, 1942, 10-11). The body of evidence thus collected is a small group of samples chosen from an immense domain. Geneticists *assume* that these samples are typical or representative of the domain as a whole; and on this basis they draw conclusions about the genetic make-up of organisms in general. No reasonable person can quarrel with such a procedure. But one can properly object if the conclusions are put forward dogmatically as incontrovertible truths. For in fact they are nothing more than probable generalizations of a limited body of evidence which is assumed to be typical of all living nature.

One can equally object if the impression is conveyed that the rôle of mutations in evolutionary causality has been clearly and finally established. As a matter of fact, responsible writers are careful not to convey this impression. Thus one of them remarks: 'It must be admitted that the direct and complete proof of the utilization of mutations in evolution under natural conditions has not yet been given . . . Thus it is inevitable that for the present we must rely mainly on the convergence of a number of separate lines of evidence, each partial and indirect or incomplete, but severally cumulative and demonstrative' (Huxley, 1942, 116). Yet here again the 'demonstration' yields only probable knowledge and is dependent upon certain assumptions which have to be made if the demonstration is to be possible at all.

Finally, it is important to remember that by their very nature genetic processes have limitations which result in their contributing little to some aspects of evolution. For example, human and immediately pre-human evolution have been profoundly influenced by the transmission of experience and knowledge from generation to generation. But the genetic mechanism cannot effect any transmission of this sort. 'It cannot . . . transmit any mental experience or any result of mental experience, but merely the capacity for having a certain kind of experience, including in some animals the capacity for learning from experience' (Huxley, 1951, 606). As we will note below, a new type of heredity, which is cultural rather than physical, has been at work in man's evolution. This does not mean that genetic processes play no causal rôle here, but only that their limitations must not be overlooked.

(ii) *Natural selection.* So far we have taken up only one of the causal conditions of evolution specified by modern selectionist theory; undirected genetic variability due to mutation, recombination, hybridization, etc. This is the source from which evolution gets its raw material. There is, however, another important causal condition in virtue of which the raw material is 'processed'. This is the phenomenon of natural selection, whose main features must now be reviewed.

It is well to observe that the term 'natural selection', like many other scientific expressions, has its roots in ordinary, non-scientific discourse. The word 'selection', for example, before it became part of the language of biology, had an established meaning in everyday language, where it designated a kind of purposive activity performed by human beings; the activity involved choosing some object, person, situation, etc, from a number of available alternatives. This is the sense in which Darwin first used the word in *The Origin of Species,* when discussing the effects of the breeding of domestic plants and animals. By 'artificial selection', men exercised a deliberate choice of the parents of each generation. Darwin then proceeded to employ the term 'natural selection' to designate a process which goes on 'under Nature', quite independently of human intervention. In this new context, 'selection' ceased to have a literal meaning, as Darwin clearly saw, and became a metaphor. Yet he argued that as long as its metaphorical meaning is borne in mind, the expression is a convenient one which should cause no difficulties. This was certainly an over-optimistic view, as subsequent developments showed.

A sounder policy is to disregard the metaphorical significance of 'natural selection', and take it as a technical expression whose meaning is fixed by its rôle in the framework of evolutionary theory. The expression can then be freed from its associations with the idea of conscious choice which arise from the use of 'selection' in everyday discourse. Instead, 'natural selection' can be understood to symbolize, at a high level of generality, a process which has gone on since the beginning of life. The process is a complex one which cannot be directly observed. Yet the reasons for holding that it occurs arise from a large body of observable facts, especially the changing characteristics of individuals and populations.

(a) *Organisms, environment and adaptation.* The first step in grasping the technical meaning of 'natural selection' is to appreciate the relations which exist between organisms and environment. The members of a population can survive only as long as they maintain a dynamic equilibrium between themselves and their surroundings. The maintaining of this equilibrium constitutes the process of adaptation, the 'fitting together' of organisms and environment to form a harmonious or balanced state of affairs. Both organisms and environment possess features which at a given moment permit the adaptive process to go on. In other words, organisms living in a particular environment manifest a 'fitness' to exist there. The environment also manifests a 'fitness' to support these organisms. The latter feature is one we will discuss at a subsequent point. Here we may simply note that the fitness of the environment is a temporal pre-condition of the adaptive process. The fitness of organisms, on the other hand, is a product of natural selection, a product analysable into a set of phenotypic characters and genotypic factors which are advantageous to the individuals possessing them. The characters and factors are often referred to as 'adaptations'.

That a particular character or factor is an adaptation cannot be discovered by observation. It can only be discovered by inference from what is observed. The inference depends on a theory embodying knowledge of how organisms maintain themselves in specific environments. Most of this knowledge is derived from the physiological and ecological study of existing organisms. But the inference also makes implicit use of the concept of 'purpose' or 'proper function' in judging that a particular character is an adaptation, the purpose or function always being related to the promoting of the viability of the organism possessing the character. Examples of this type of inference abound in the literature of zoology and botany (Cf. Smith, 1958). Thus, the resemblance of the closed wings of the butterfly *Kallima* to a dead leaf is judged to be an adaptation, since its purpose is to enable the insect to escape detection by predators. The succulent leaves of desert plants are judged to be an adaptation, since their proper function is to store water for the plants to use during long periods of drought. And so on. Undoubtedly, inference of this kind has its dangers. It also creates special problems when

G

applied to fossil materials (Cf. Davis, 1949). Yet the inference seems essential to the specifying of adaptations. Hence as will be argued below, the idea of purpose is bound to play some part, if only a minor one, in evolutionary theory.

It is tempting to suppose that adaptation must be an all-or-none process. This supposition seems to have been implicit in a criticism which used to be advanced against Darwinism, and sometimes still is (Cf. Cannon, 1958). An organism is either adapted to its environment, the criticism runs, or it is not. If it is adapted, the organism survives. If it is not adapted, it succumbs. This argument leads to the conclusion that natural selection cannot account for the occurrence of evolutionary changes in viable organisms. For any change which takes place in an adapted organism will upset its harmonious adjustment to the environment, and therefore lead to its elimination in the struggle for existence. This is particularly evident where adaptation depends on the functioning of a complicated organ such as the vertebrate eye. The effective operation of the eye demands the co-ordinated activity of numerous parts. Hence even the slightest change in one of these parts will disrupt this co-ordination and result in the loss of the adaptive value of that organ. This in turn will lead to the extinction of the animal whose adaptation required the organ's proper functioning. Here, surely, is a dilemma from which Darwinism cannot escape.

One reply to this criticism is that it mistakenly assumes that adaptation is either present or absent. But in fact adaptation is subject to different degrees, so that there is a 'scale of fitness' whose upper limit is a condition of optimum adaptation and whose lower limit is the least degree of adaptation which can exist without leading to loss of viability. Organs whose functioning falls beneath the lower limit may be said to display 'maladaptation'. Maladaptations do not necessarily result in the immediate extinction of organisms possessing them, but they do result in ultimate extinction. An actual population is such that its individual members are spread out in accordance with the scale of fitness, the greatest density occurring as a rule near the upper end. Accordingly, there is a wide range within which an individual's adaptation may vary. Minimal adaptation does not destroy an individual's viability, and even maladaptation need not do so instantly. In short, adaptation is far from being a simple 'all-or-none' affair.

If evolution is to go on, not only individual organisms but also populations must be viable. As one generation of a continuing population disappears, it is replaced by the next generation. Hence from the standpoint of evolution a vitally important group of adaptations consists of those which facilitate reproduction. A population's 'fitness' depends, therefore, on adaptive characters which enable its members to survive and reproduce at a rate which does not fall permanently below the death-rate of the population. This is still not the full story, for a population's fitness also depends on the 'adaptability' of its individual constituents. The significance of this property can be better understood if something further is said about the environment and its modes of change.

The temptation to oversimplify is nowhere stronger than in discussions of the way the environment influences adaptation. There is a tendency to assume that for biological purposes the environment is simple and homogeneous, whereas it is in reality extraordinarily complex. The complexity is so great, indeed, that an exhaustive description of it cannot be given; or, at any rate, cannot be other than an ideal limit to which description may try to approximate. It will be sufficient for our purposes to mention certain large-scale aspects and to ignore details. Thus 'the environment' of a particular local population includes: (i) the purely physical or abiotic *milieu* in which the population exists, including its geographical location, the prevailing climatic conditions, terrain, etc; (ii) the organic or biotic *milieu*, including the non-living organic matter and all the other local populations of plants and animals in that region. For each individual member of the population, 'the environment' includes, in addition to (i) and (ii), the other members of its population, i.e. the intra-deme environment. Perhaps there should also be included 'the internal environment' formed by the individual's own body (Cf. Simpson, 1953).

Since a description of literally *all* the aspects of the environment is impossible in practice, it follows *a fortiori* that we cannot hope to describe all the possible kinds of environmental change. It will be enough to mention a few that are common. Thus among the kinds of change to which the abiotic environment is subject are: (i) climatic alterations such as shifts in annual mean temperature, rainfall, etc; (ii) crustal alterations such as mountain building, erosion, etc; and (iii) violent changes due to floods, droughts, volcanic eruptions, etc. Among the kinds of change characteristic of the biotic environment are: (a) increase, reduction, or disappearance of the food supply upon which a particular local population depends; and (b) colonization of the population's habitat by new groups of competitors, predators, etc. Sometimes a population will through its own actions produced a marked change in its environment (e.g. beavers); or the population may move from an existing habitat to one that is more suitable (e.g. the migration of birds). Such cases show that it is wrong to think of adaptations as *imposed on* the organism by the environment. They are rather the product of an interaction between the environment and the organism.

It may be doubted whether from the standpoint of evolution an environment is ever absolutely stable. Some changes in it are always occurring. Hence it is sound to think of these changes as forming a scale or 'environmental gradient' which extends from minimal to maximal. A situation of minimal change may be said to be one of relative stability. Now as previously indicated, since in every local population adaptive traits vary from member to member, these traits also can be thought of as forming a scale or 'character-gradient' in accordance with the degree of their adequacy in promoting the fitness of individuals. For the latter are not all equally well adapted to their environment. No method is available at present for estimating quantitatively the precise degree of individual adaptation. But it is at least clear that the scale of fitness has a lower limit represented by the minimal degree of adaptation compatible with viability, i.e. with the capacity of individuals to grow to maturity, to endure for some time as adults, and to leave offspring. Above this limit, significant differences in viability always exist. Hence, even a population in a relatively stable environment does not exhibit absolute uniformity of adaptation on the part of its members.

When environmental change is accelerated, the fitness of individuals and populations depends upon their adaptability rather than upon their adaptation. In the case of individuals this means that their genotypes must permit the modification of existing phenotypic characters or the development of new ones. But since the genotype is fixed in the case of each individual, the latter's adaptability will be relatively slight. Indeed, the more the individual's adaptation to a given environment approaches the optimum, the less able it is to cope with any large environmental change. Some organisms are so perfectly adapted to a specific habitat that it is impossible for them to live in any other. Even small environmental changes are fatal to them. On the other hand, organisms near the lower limit of the scale of fitness in a given habitat may tolerate or thrive on a marked alteration of it. This phenomenon has been called 'the survival of the incompletely adapted', and has been regarded as more important for evolution than the older notion of 'the survival of the fittest' (Cf. Wood Jones, 1953).

The capacity of a population to survive large environmental changes depends mainly on (i) the supply of heritable variability stored in its 'gene pool'; and (ii) the range of variation determined by whatever new mutations are possible for the genetic factors constituting the pool. Condition (i) is a consequence of the particulate nature of heredity. The gene pool of a population, or of a group of populations forming a species, contains, in addition to the genes controlling existing adaptations, a store of genes which may have arisen far apart in space and time, and which may give rise to precisely those adaptations appropriate to the changed environmental circumstances. 'These life-saving genes may have been present in the species for a million years as a result of long past mutations, without having been of any value to the species. Now, under changed conditions, they may save it from extinction' (Allee, 1951, 85). This 'concealed potential variability' is the major basis of a population's or a species' capacity for survival. New mutations, as specified in (ii), will usually be of supplementary significance only. With the slowing down of environmental change, a population tends to approach a condition of relative stability by means of a fresh set of adaptive traits. It is worth remembering that adaptability, like adaptation, may have many different degrees, determined by such things as the size of the population, the extent to which the population contains partially isolated sub-groups, etc. But this subject involves details into which we need not enter.

Some students have given prominence to what are called 'preadaptations', a term which 'has been applied to a great variety of real or supposed evolutionary phenomena' (Simpson, 1953, 188). There appears to be at least one sense of this term which is quite acceptable. If a species has managed to survive a major environmental change, it can appropriately be said to have possessed some phenotypic characteristics 'preadapted' to the later environmental conditions. For in order to effect the transition from the earlier to the later environment, the species has to maintain a minimal adaptation throughout. Certain 'preadapted characters' are therefore required to make the transition possible. In this general sense, 'preadaptation' is not a special kind of adaptation, but simply a universal feature of the adaptive process.

There are, however, some more controversial uses of the term which may be mentioned. Suppose that a species has survived a change from one sort of environment E_1 to another sort E_2; and that a certain characteristic C has remained structurally the same during the transition. C may be described as 'preadapted' to E_2 in each of the following cases: (i) C is the basis of one kind of adaptive function in E_1 and a different kind of adaptive function in E_2; (ii) C is adaptively neutral in E_1 and adaptive in E_2; and (iii) C is adaptively disadvantageous in E_1 and adaptive in E_2. The controversial element here arises from the difficulty of finding clear-cut examples of the three cases in evolutionary history. Case (i) is probably the least troublesome. Authorities such as Cuénot (1932) and Carter (1951) have adduced a number of examples of this sort of 'preadaptation'—most of them involving changes of habit in animals. The admission of such examples does not commit one to any doctrine of a purposive agency which has arranged in advance that C shall perform a dual function. For one may hold, as Carter does, that the correlation of C with both E_1 and E_2 is entirely a matter of chance. Cases (ii) and (iii) depend upon the acceptability of the idea of adaptively neutral and adaptively disadvantageous characters as genuine occurrents in evolution. Does modern selectionist theory countenance such characters? Or must all characters of a viable organism have some adaptive value? Since interesting consequences depend on the answers to these questions, it will be well to take note of the issues involved.

The early followers of Darwin tended to hold that every phenotypic character which survives has some adaptive value. This view was quite unproven, and would find few supporters today. Some biologists still hold, however, that every character must be *assumed* to be adaptive, even when it cannot be shown that this is the case, because the persistence of neutral or disadvantageous characters is incompatible with the operation of selection. One consequence which has been derived from this assumption is that the various mental or psychical traits manifested by Homo sapiens must be preserved because of their utility in promoting survival. Hence the human mind, like the wings of a bird or the gills of a fish, is an adaptive mechanism. The concepts and theories it produces are 'instruments' to facilitate man's adaptation to the physical environment. They function as guides for his practical activity. This was one of the conclusions drawn from Darwinism by Bergson. It is a conclusion which follows from the premiss that all characters of viable organisms must be adaptive.

In recent years a number of biologists have been led to recognize the possibility of non-adaptive or inadaptive characters occurring in otherwise well adapted organisms. These characters are never numerous, and it is admittedly difficult to prove of any one that it has absolutely no adaptive value. Yet the evidence of genetics shows how such characters can arise. For it is known that many genes are pleiotropic, i.e. have more than one phenotypic effect. Hence one effect of a given gene may be highly advantageous to the organism carrying it, while another effect of the same gene may be non-advantageous or slightly disadvantageous. Both sorts of effects will be manifested by the organisms concerned. Furthermore, students of the genetics of populations have shown how a gene determining a non-adaptive character may become fixed in a species as a result of a process called 'genetic drift', which can occur in small, isolated groups. The upshot is that contemporary evolutionary theory cannot be said to require that every character of a viable organism must be adaptive. Some characters very likely are adaptively neutral (e.g. minute details of colour pattern in insects or of shell sculpturing in brachiopods) and even mildly disadvantageous. Thus the possibility remains open that the human mind is not just a biologically adaptive device. Concepts and theories may not be simply instruments for promoting man's adaptation to the physical world. We will discuss this issue a little more in another chapter.

Returning to the question of preadaptation, it would appear that cases (ii) and (iii) above must be admitted as actual though infrequent, occurrences in evolution. If non-adaptive or inadaptive traits can be preserved in a population, there is no reason why they should not turn out to be adaptive when the population successfully meets a major environmental change. Such a phenomenon seems to have occurred from time to time in evolutionary history. Simpson remarks of case (iii), which he calls 'true preadaptation', that while it is no doubt extremely rare, it 'provides a mechanism for sudden and erratic changes in adaptive type. The importance of such an event could be great, even though its occurrence were markedly exceptional' (Simpson, 1949, 236-37). Admitting that preadaptations have a place in the evolutionary picture undoubtedly implies some limitation of the scope of natural selection. Yet it can still be held that in the vast majority of instances selection is what determines fitness.

To sum up the main considerations of this section, I will outline a model of organism-environment relationships which is due to Wright (1932). He represents the environment of living things as a rugged terrain consisting of a large, but finite, number of peaks and valleys. Some of the peaks stand by themselves in relative isolation. Others are parts of 'mountain ranges', whose individual pinnacles are separated from one another by relatively shallow depressions. Each of the peaks symbolizes a particular ecological niche, and each population of organisms is conceived as occupying one of them. None of the valleys, however, is permanently occupied. Now on a peak, the members of a population possessing optimum adaptation are clustered at the very top. Those whose adaptation falls below the optimum are strung out in steadily decreasing numbers down the slopes. The pressure of selection is what keeps the best adapted populations always at the summit of a peak and leaves the valleys uninhabited.

Since a population can be regarded abstractly as an assemblage of genes, it has been suggested by Dobzhansky that we visualize the field of their possible combinations in the form of a topographic map of the above terrain. The 'contours' of the map will symbolize the adaptive value of various gene-combinations. 'Groups of related combinations of genes, which make the organisms that possess them able to occupy certain ecological niches, are then represented by the "adaptive peaks" situated in different parts of the field. The unfavourable combinations of genes, which make their carriers unfit to live in any existing environment, are represented by the "adaptive valleys" which lie between the peaks' (Dobzhansky, 1951, 9). The model thus provides a way of symbolizing the totality of conceivable gene-combinations, graded with respect to their fitness to survive in terrestrial environments.

To make the model exemplify evolutionary changes, dynamic elements have to be incorporated in it. This can be done by means of two suppositions. First, we suppose that the peaks alter in size, some of the biggest becoming small and some of the smallest, big. Occasionally, a wholly new peak will spring up. These alterations represent the constantly changing character of the environments in which organisms live. Secondly, we suppose that under the pressure of selection a population may leave its original peak, cross a valley, and climb another peak. In the vast majority of cases this will happen because of the occurrence of a mutation among some of the population (usually those on the slopes rather than on the summit), by virtue of which they are able to shift to a fresh habitat. On rare occasions, however, no mutations are involved. Random fluctuations of gene ratios may be sufficient to carry a population to the bottom of a valley and on to the slope of another peak which it will then proceed to climb under the influence of selection. 'In this case, the direction in which evolutionary change goes on, i.e. the choice of which hill is ascended, is under the control of chance, though in a long enough period the broadest, and therefore probably the highest hill (representing the fittest population) is likely to be reached. Over a long period, then, the chance element in evolution is less important' (Waddington, 1939, 293). As a population climbs a new peak, it undergoes changes which result in new phenotypic traits being manifested by the bulk of its members.

While the above model is a valuable device for thinking about organism-environment relationships, it has obvious limitations, as Wright himself did not fail to point out. Like every model it greatly oversimplifies the situation which it represents. In the present case, for example, there is nothing to symbolize the relation of a population to other populations on a given peak (competitors in the same ecological niche), and, even more evidently, nothing to represent the process of selection. But one model cannot be expected to embrace every feature of adaptive situations.

(b) *Selection and Population Changes.* The next step in appreciating the technical meaning of natural selection is to see how it is connected with the basic sort of evolution. It will be recalled that the statistical models discussed in Chapter II, Section 5, show evolution at the primary level to be a systematic alteration in the pattern of gene frequencies in a population. Between one generation and the next there occurs a non-random change of heritable factors, and this change is at least in principle statistically describable. Now it is generally agreed that genetic processes alone (i.e. mutation, random recombination, and random fixation or elimination) are insufficient to account for what happens in this situation. That is to say, genetic processes by themselves would result in population changes very much slower than those actually indicated by paleontological evidence. Hence, 'some factor additional to strictly genetic processes is required to explain many observed rates of evolution, and the most reasonable probability is that the factor was selection' (Simpson, 1953, 146). The main components of this factor, taken in relation to the basic evolutionary process, will now be outlined.

It has already been noted that the members of a population exhibit different degrees of adaptation to their environment. One of the results of this is that they have varying degrees of success in remaining alive. Some individuals live only for a short time, while others live longer. Hence in the population a process of differential survival occurs, and this is the central component of Darwinian natural selection. But there is another result of adaptational differences which has come to be recognized as important. Among those members of the population who reach maturity, some have more offspring than others. This is the process of differential reproduction. It is specifiable in terms of the average number of offspring in each generation of the population, and the various deviations from the average. Differential reproduction has become the central component in the modern theory of natural selection, displacing differential survival and thus enlarging classical Darwinian doctrine.

Why was the enlargement required? The answer is broadly that Darwinian selection is not a necessary condition of the basic evolutionary process. Simpson has aptly illustrated this point as follows:

'Suppose that all the individuals in a population lived for precisely the same length of time, with no elimination of the unfit or survival of the fittest, hence no Darwinian selection. Suppose, further, that those among them systematically definable as, say, the taller ones or those . . . with a hereditary fondness for apples, had twice as many offspring as those without these characteristics. Then there would be very strong, clearly non-Darwinian selection, and under its influence extremely rapid (although short-range) evolution of the population' (Simpson, 1953, 138).

Thus differential reproduction would give rise to an orderly change in the pattern of gene frequencies exhibited by the population, so that the genes controlling tallness and fondness for apples would spread rapidly through the population in a few generations. Here evolution occurs without differential survival.

There are, nevertheless, situations in which Darwinian selection, i.e. the death or survival of certain individuals, does contribute to evolution at the primary level. 'Elimination of less well adapted or, in Darwinian terms, less fit variants in a population will have a non-random effect on gene frequencies, provided that the eliminated individuals are, on the average, different genetically from those that survive, and provided that they are eliminated before they have had an average number of offspring' (Simpson, 1950b, V). Hence differential survival may result in systematic differential reproduction, but does not necessarily do so. Another way of putting the matter is to say that Darwinian selection is a special case of selection in the wider, statistical sense. Accordingly, it is less than accurate to describe modern selectionist theory as 'Neo-Darwinian', though it is certainly not to be described as 'anti-Darwinian'.

It is not hard to see that differential reproduction is itself affected by a great number of factors. Such things as the choice of females by the male members of the population, the competition of males for females, competition for food, various environmental influences, etc, all tend to result in some individuals producing more offspring and others producing less. Each of these factors may be regarded as a type of selection and be given a separate title (e.g. 'sexual selection', 'intra-sexual selection', 'intra-specific selection', etc). But the feature common to them all is that of engendering differential reproduction. Hence, the view we are considering may be summarized by saying that the core of natural selection is differential reproduction tending to produce orderly genetic changes in populations.

Two amendments of classical Darwinism can now be made in the light of this analysis. (i) It will be recalled that because of the influence of Malthus' Essay, Darwin contended that excessive reproduction, i.e. reproduction at approximately a geometric rate, is characteristic of all living things. But it is clear that 'the production of offspring is only excessive in relation to an imaginary world, and the "high geometrical rate of increase" is only attained by abolishing a real death rate, while retaining a

real rate of reproduction' (Fisher, 1930, 43). Actually, most
organisms produce just about the number of offspring required
to ensure the continuation of their kind. Stable populations show
a reproductive rate broadly equal to the rate of elimination.
'Nidicolous birds, Lack has shown, illustrate this truth with particular clarity; they do in fact lay clutches of a certain size,
though they could lay more eggs . . . and could, of course, lay
fewer. Having regard to all the exigencies of giving birth to and
rearing eggs and young, the size of its clutch is just about that
which gives each species its greatest likelihood of self-perpetua-
tion' (Medawar, 1957, 15). (ii) If the doctrine of reproduction at
a geometric rate is untenable, then it cannot legitimately serve
as one of the premises from which natural selection is inferred.
Darwin argued that since too many offspring of a species are
born to be supported by the available food supply, large numbers
of the young have to be eliminated so that the species can continue
to exist. From here he went on to infer the occurrence of natural
selection. But this puts the cart before the horse, since the degree
of fecundity is itself a consequence of natural selection, not vice
versa. If a continuing species has a high mortality rate among its
young, then selection has resulted in it having a high birth-rate,
otherwise the species would have become extinct. Similarly, if the
death-rate among the young is low and the density of the population fairly stable, selection has resulted in its having a low
birth-rate. In short, once we recognize that the basis of selection
is differential reproduction, we can discard the Malthusian notion
of 'excessive reproduction', along with Darwin's attempt to use
it as a premiss from which selection is to be inferred.

Classical Darwinism was often thought to imply that individual organisms were passive in relation to the evolutionary
process. They were not responsible for the variations which
occurred in successive generations. Each organism was acted on
by the force of natural selection, and by its own behaviour could
contribute nothing to the subsequent history of the species. This
misconception should now be exploded for all time. For what we
refer to as the process of differential reproduction is simply the
combined result of the behaviour of all the individual organisms
which compose a population. So far from their activity being
irrelevant to the course of evolution, it is precisely the statistical
consequences of this activity which enter into the determination
of that course. No doubt one of the reasons why this misconcep-

tion arose in the first place was inherent in the expression 'natural selection' itself, as we will shortly indicate.

Our outline of this complex subject may be concluded by adding some comments on a few supplementary points. (i) Where Darwinian selection was exclusively concerned with phenotypic characters, the enlarged doctrine permits direct selective action on the genotype. 'Genetic factors without consistent phenotypic correlation may nevertheless influence fertility and therefore be subject to selection not acting on or through the phenotype' (Simpson, 1953, 139). (ii) Selection as currently conceived is not an absolute constant, but varies in intensity. This fact is often expressed by saying that there are differences of 'selection pressure' in populations of different kinds. In a given population selection pressure may be high for one or more characters and low for others. But it is probably never the case that selection pressure is zero for all characters, though the pressure may be so mild in small, isolated populations as to allow non-selective changes to occur. This is the phenomenon of 'genetic drift' already mentioned. As a result of it genes may be preserved or destroyed quite irrespective of their adaptive value. Genetic drift is, however, a comparatively rare occurrence; and, as its discoverer, Sewall Wright, has emphasized, the effects on a population are usually degenerative and a 'prelude to extinction' (Wright, 1948). (iii) If selection be viewed abstractly, it is possible to distinguish certain 'directional' features of it. For example, where a 'typical' or modal character of a population existing in a stable environment has greater adaptive value than any variant character, selection will act so as to eliminate the variant forms. In this case, its direction is said to be 'centripetal', concentrating the population around a point which is the optimum condition. On the other hand, where the modal character has less adaptive value than the variants, selection will be 'centrifugal', favouring increase in variation and leading to progressive divergence from the population mean. 'Linear' direction can also be defined (Cf. Simpson, 1953). Because selection has both intensity and direction, it is sometimes regarded as a 'vector'.

(iii) *Selection as a Directive Factor.* The genetic factors in evolution are reckoned to be 'random' or 'undirected' in the sense discussed above. Natural selection, however, is often described as a 'non-random' or 'directive' factor. We must next clarify what is meant by such a description.

A simple model put forward by Muller (1929a; 1949) provides an illuminating approach to this question. The model depicts a world of organisms whose genetic make-up and reproductive mechanisms are exactly like those which prevail on the earth, but whose activities do not give rise to natural selection. There is neither differential survival nor differential multiplication in the world of the model. No offspring of any organism or pair of organisms fails to reach maturity and to reproduce; and each organism or pair of organisms gives rise to the same number of offspring. Now given sufficient time, the random multiplication of variations in this world will produce step by step and in the same sequence all the forms of life which have appeared in the course of terrestrial evolution. At a certain point in the history of the model we will find an exact duplication of the populations, species, genera, families, etc, at present inhabiting the earth.

'However, in that case the forms corresponding to our living ones, though in absolute numbers as great as today, would be so vanishingly few, relatively to the total, as to be lost in it. For that total, including all the conceivable "misfits", would be so stupendous as not to be containable in a universe of universes. An indefinitely continued and quite unrestricted multiplication of variations, then, would in the end, through the sheer numbers attained, give opportunity for the most improbable of all arrangements, namely complexly working adaptive organizations like ourselves, to come into existence without design. They represent, however, the almost infinitely rare, the most select combination of chances' (Muller, 1949, 460).

Several important conclusions can be drawn with the aid of this model. (a) Existing organic forms represent an infinitesimally minute proportion of the possible organic forms which would result from genetic recombination and mutation in a multiplication process not subject to natural selection. Muller has calculated that the total possible organic forms constitute 'a stupendous, ghostly army of potential creatures, involving a total of $100^{1,500}$ to $10,000^{1,000,000}$, or maybe many more, possible combinations...' (Muller, 1929a, 504). In the light of the complete range of possibilities, existing organic forms are a 'highly improbable' collection of beings. If recent conclusions about the internal structure of the gene are taken into account, this high improbability is fantastically increased (Cf. Muller, 1958). (b) The actual existence of such an army of organisms would be physically impossible in the spatio-temporal universe as we know it. 'If there were this many beings actually produced, then even if each being were as small as an electron, and all beings were packed tightly together, there would not be nearly enough room in the entire Einsteinian universe . . . for even an insignificant tittle of them' (Muller, 1929, 504). (c) Accordingly, some factor must be operative in restricting organisms to those actually produced in terrestrial evolution. It seems clear that this factor is natural selection. It would be a little more precise to say that the factor is natural selection in its negative or eliminative rôle. Since the result is the generation of a determinate order out of random genetic elements, it is quite appropriate to describe this rôle as 'directive'.

But there is another facet of the matter which needs to be emphasized. Natural selection does not merely *prevent* the vast majority of possible genotypes from being brought into existence. It also has the positive or constructive rôle of building up certain genotypes and spreading them through a population in successive generations. This happens by virtue of differential reproduction. To elucidate the constructive rôle of natural selection, Simpson (1947) has delineated a model which may be regarded as supplementary to that of Muller.

In Simpson's model, the genetic factors are represented by an enormous pool of all the letters of the alphabet in equal abundance. Selection is represented by the following activity. A sequence of draws from the pool is begun, three letters being taken on each draw, with a view to producing the word 'cat'. Only the letters c, a and t are put back in the pool if they are drawn in wrong combinations; all the other letters are discarded. When any two of the favourable letters are drawn simultaneously, they are clipped together and returned to the pool. A pair so clipped may later be one of the items in a draw. The word 'cat' is taken to represent any viable genotype or organism.

Now the probability of getting the desired combination of letters at the opening draw is extremely small. On the supposition that the pool contains 1,000 complete alphabets, there are roughly three million million possible combinations of three letters, and only a relatively few of these are favourable. It is highly improbable that one of the favourable combinations will be drawn if no letters are ever replaced in the pool. But if we follow the method prescribed by the model, and replace only the favourable letters and clip pairs of favourable letters, we rapidly increase the probability of getting the desired result. For it will not take many draws to leave in the pool an enormous preponderance of clipped *ct, ca* and *at* combinations, together with a supply of *c*'s, *a*'s and *t*'s needed to complete any one of these combinations if it is drawn again. Thus by adopting the special method of the model, 'you have "generated a high degree of improbability"—you have made it probable that you will quickly achieve the combination *cat* which was so improbable at the outset. Moreover, you have created something. You did not create the letters *c, a* and *t*, but you have created the word "cat" which did not exist when you started' (Simpson, 1947, 493).

These two models enable us to perceive the appropriateness of describing selection as a 'directive' factor in evolution. For on the negative side it prevents the vast majority of genotypes from seeing the light of day, and eliminates unfit genotypes by ensuring that their carriers have no offspring or the fewest offspring in a given population. On the positive side, selection determines what genetic materials will be utilized in evolution and how they will be assembled to produce an organized result. The models likewise enable us to see the point of the aphorism attributed to Fisher, that 'selection is a mechanism for generating an extremely high degree of improbability' (Cf. Huxley, 1942; 1951; 1953). For it is by virtue of this mechanism that an outcome which is *genetically* most unlikely becomes in fact practically inevitable. That is to say, selection makes highly probable certain genetic combinations which would otherwise be highly improbable. A process having such consequences is quite appropriately called directive.

We can now realize how wide of the mark are those who have argued that selectionist theory cannot be true because it must represent the course of evolution as 'wholly due to chance'. For it is precisely the point of the theory that selection is an 'anti-chance' factor, which tends to produce systematic and orderly changes in populations. The genetic factors operate in a random manner, but selection certainly does not. Furthermore, 'the old arguments about the impossibility of imagining that "chance" could create a hand or eye or other complex adaptive organ, no longer carry any weight. In fact, the "argument from improbability" has now recoiled on the heads of its users, and the apparently incredible complication of an organ must now be taken as additional evidence for the power of natural selection. . . . The geneticist, fortified by a quantitative grasp of natural selection, can say "*credo quia improbabile*" ' (Huxley, 1951, 595). The more elaborate and remarkable an adaptation is, the more it testifies to the efficacy of selection.

These considerations can be connected with a matter referred to at the beginning of the chapter. I there suggested that the feeling of wonder excited in many minds by the panorama of evolution has at least two sources. One of the sources is the sense of the colossal improbability of what has happened in the history of life, when this history is imaginatively contemplated from the standpoint of the first living things. The other source is the recognition of the astonishing harmony exhibited by organic nature, each type of organism fitting neatly into its environmental niche, as though it were part of a prearranged design. Modern selectionist theory provides a plausible explanation for both of these reactions. It shows that there is a perfectly intelligible sense in which the course of evolution *has been* a highly improbable sequence of events. It also shows that the same factors which gave rise to this sequence are responsible for the detailed adaptations of organisms to their environmental niches, and hence for the appearance of design in living nature. Additional weight is thereby given to the theory, since it not only accounts for a wide range of objective facts but also gives a plausible account of why these facts generate certain feelings and impressions in man.

(iv) *Misleading Formulations of Selectionist Theory*. The language in which selectionist theory has been expressed has not always been free from certain misleading formulations. This is particularly true of classical Darwinian doctrine. It will therefore be appropriate to comment on some of the expressions which have proved to be trouble-makers.

'*Competition*' *and the* '*Struggle for Existence*'. We have already noted that for Darwin natural selection involved a process of differential survival. Only a fraction of the seeds and fertilized eggs produced ever reached the adult stage. We have also noted that Darwin considered differential survival, at least in the animal kingdom, to be the result of competition of individuals for food and other requirements of life. Now this competition seems to have been envisaged by him as generally, or perhaps always, a violent affair, i.e. a literal 'struggle for existence'. Despite his

H

remark that he used the latter expression in a broad and meta-phorical sense, it is apparent from much that he says that he regarded physical combat, predatory activity, the destruction of the weaker by the stronger, and the survival of the most ruthless individuals and species, as essential to evolution. Without such continual violence, natural selection would cease to function. Hence, T. H. Huxley referred to the Darwinian doctrine as 'the gladiatorial theory of existence', and Tennyson spoke of 'nature red in tooth and claw'.

This gladiatorial conception of evolution was largely due to the influence on Darwin of the ideas of Malthus. In Chapter III of *An Essay on the Principles of Population* (1798), Malthus intro-duced the expression 'struggle for existence' to describe a situa-tion frequent in the life of primitive men. 'When they fell in with any tribes like their own, the contest was a struggle for existence, and they fought with desperate courage, inspired by the reflection that death was the punishment for defeat and life the prize of victory. In these savage contests many tribes . . . were utterly exterminated . . .' (1798, 47-8). Behind this notion lay the Mal-thusian doctrine that populations inevitably increase at a rate which produces a condition of food scarcity and overcrowding. The only effective check to such increase at the sub-human level is fierce competition leading to the death of large numbers of individuals. Many of Darwin's conclusions were obviously in-fluenced by this doctrine.

In the closing decades of the nineteenth century, the gladia-torial conception of evolution, epitomized by the terms 'competi-tion' and 'struggle for existence', exercised a profound effect on various minds. To such men as Drummond and Kropotkin it was an utterly false conception. The former's *The Ascent of Man* (1894) and the latter's *Mutual Aid* (1902) were written to show how false it was. To others it constituted a problem. Thus, T. H. Huxley in his Romanes Lecture, 'Evolution and Ethics' (1893), was led to the conclusion that the ethical progress of society depends not on imitating the struggle for existence in nature, or on running away from it, but on combating it. To still others, the gladiatorial conception was a profound truth, not only about organic nature, but also about human society. Hence arose the group of ideas known as 'social Darwinism', espoused by such men as Spencer in England, Haeckel in Germany, and Sumner in the United States.

From the vantage point of the present, this controversy appears wholly misguided. It arose partly because of an inadequate understanding of natural selection and partly because the popular connotations of 'competition' and 'struggle for existence' were so misleading. The core of natural selection, as we have seen, is systematic differential reproduction. Under certain conditions, but by no means always, this will result from differential survival. Now differential survival in turn can result from the combat of individuals and the destruction of some individuals by others, i.e. it can result from 'competition' and the 'struggle for existence' as understood by the Darwinians. But differential survival can also come about in entirely non-violent ways. For example, if a population of bacteria is placed in a test-tube containing nutrient broth, the bacteria will multiply to the point where numbers of them will fail to survive. We may describe this situation by saying that the individual bacteria 'compete' with each other, in the sense that the more food any of them consumes, the less there will be for the others. Yet clearly the bacteria do not engage in violent combat or destroy each other. Similarly, when two species of grass are growing in the same meadow, they may be said to 'struggle' with each other in the sense that only a limited amount of space is available for their growth and multiplication. Numerous seeds will be unable to survive in this 'struggle'. But here again no gladiatorial strife or victory of the more ruthless species occurs. In both cases differential survival comes about 'peacefully'. Darwin may have had this kind of situation in mind when he described the expression 'struggle for existence' as a metaphor. Yet the popular connotation of the expression, and of 'competition' (derived from their use in characterizing certain kinds of human behaviour), made it fatally easy to engender misconceptions (Dobzhansky, 1950a).

There can be little doubt, then, that natural selection does not require combative and predatory activity. 'Advantage in differential reproduction is usually a peaceful process in which the concept of struggle is irrelevant' (Simpson, 1949, 222). The same is true of evolution. Much of it goes on without violent conflict. The gladiatorial conception is therefore a nineteenth century myth. No one denies, of course, that 'competition' and 'struggle' in the Darwinian sense do often occur in nature, and may function as evolutionary agencies. But they may also function as counter-evolutionary agencies under certain circumstances, by rendering species less fit to cope with their environment (Haldane, 1932).

The restoring of a more accurate viewpoint on this whole matter has been accompanied by a recognition that the expressions 'co-operation' and 'mutual help' have a legitimate place in the formulation of evolutionary theory alongside 'competition' and 'struggle'. It thus appears that Kropotkin and Drummond were right in opposing the gladiatorial conception of evolution. They were wrong in thinking that to accept co-operation as an evolutionary factor is to reject natural selection. They were also wrong if they intended to suggest that competition and struggle play no positive part in promoting evolution. 'The fact is that both competition and co-operation are observed in nature. Natural selection is neither egotistic nor altruistic. It is rather opportunistic; life is promoted now by struggle and now by mutual help' (Dobzhansky, 1955, 113). On the whole, however, it is probably true, as various people have argued, that evolution favours co-operating rather than dis-operating groups (Montagu, 1952).

'The Survival of the Fittest.' Closely connected with 'competition' and the 'struggle for existence' is another well-known expression—'the survival of the fittest'. This was first used by Spencer, and was subsequently accepted by Darwin as synonymous with 'natural selection'. Despite the fact that 'the survival of the fittest' has frequently been subjected to hostile criticism, the precise difficulties to which it gives rise have not always been made clear. It is also true that the difficulties appear at present in a somewhat different light than they did in Spencer's time.

The most obvious misleading feature of the expression is due to the superlative form of the adjective it contains. This superlative suggests that in an evolving population there are two possibilities: (a) a single individual ('the fittest') ultimately survives and all the rest die; or (b) of four broad groups of individuals—the unfit, the fit, the fitter, and the fittest—only the last survives. Neither of these absurd possibilities, of course, is realized in nature. For, as we have seen, the fitness of the members of a population can be represented as a continuous scale with a lower limit. Some organisms born in the population are such that they fall below the limit and hence fail to survive. Those which do survive are 'fit', though not in the same degree; they may, for instance, vary greatly in respect of their success in leaving progeny. What we have, then, is not 'the survival of the fittest', but simply the survival of the fit. The use of the superlative form of the adjective is quite unwarranted.

The situation referred to by the expression may be clarified a little further if we take up a standard objection which runs as follows. Exponents of natural selection say that it produces a 'survival of the fittest' (or of 'the fit'). But when we enquire 'Who are the fit?', the answer is, 'Those who survive.' Accordingly, the expression 'survival of the fit' really means 'the survival of those who survive', and so is redundant. Translated into a statement (e.g. 'All who survive are survivors'), it becomes an empty tautology.

This objection will not hold water, either logically or factually. Let us take the logical point first. It is fair to regard the expression 'survival of the fit' as expandable into the statement, 'All organisms which survive are fit'. Logically, this is a universal affirmative statement. Hence it is not equivalent to 'All fit organisms survive', though it is formally equivalent to 'No unfit organisms survive'. 'All organisms which survive are fit' is, therefore, far from being tautological.

From a factual standpoint, it is also true that 'individual survival' and 'individual fitness' are by no means identical in reference. 'If one sparrow perishes on its first weak flight from the nest, and another does not, it does not follow that the first sparrow was less fit than the second—or indeed differed from it in any significant way at all. It may have been that there happened to be a cat in the neighbourhood in one case and not in the other' (Agar, 1943, 173). Differential survival may thus arise from purely contingent environmental circumstances, i.e. those which do not form part of the standard or normal environment of the organisms concerned. But this is much less common than differential survival resulting from the possessing of phenotypic and genotypic traits which render the organism viable. Factually, then, 'survival of the fit' may be understood to mean (a) that as a general rule death or survival of the individual depends on phenotypic and genotypic traits rather than on environmental accidents, and (b) that adaptively advantageous traits are heritable.

If we wish to make 'survival of the fit' synonymous with 'natural selection', we will have to regard 'the fit' as a shorthand expression for 'those members of a population which have the most progeny', and 'survival' as a shorthand expression for 'the orderly spread of certain types of genetic constitution through a population'. This respecification of meaning is, however, not only artificial, but can also generate misunderstandings. For example, the 'fit' individuals on this approach are simply the most fecund, and not necessarily the most vigorous or hardy. Indeed, an individual organism may exhibit abnormal fecundity and yet be deficient in vigour; while low fecundity or sterility are perfectly compatible with individual strength and durability (Dobzhansky, 1950). Likewise, 'survival' in this sense has no intrinsic connection with the individual's chances of existing for the period of time which is normal for members of its population. The survival involved is that of certain genotypes, not of any one of their carriers. On the whole, then, it is better to avoid equating 'natural selection' with 'survival of the fit'. The latter expression has a more limited meaning; and even when used in the more limited way, it needs to be hedged about with safeguards to prevent misunderstanding.

'*Natural Selection as an Active Power.*' In pointing out the metaphorical character of the term 'natural selection', Darwin defended himself against the charge that he regarded selection 'as an active power or Deity', by urging that this was merely a *façon de parler* adopted in the interests of brevity. It is no more misleading, he remarked, than 'speaking of the attraction of gravity as ruling the movement of the planets.' Yet many of his opponents (and some of his followers) thought of selection as literally a power which acted on populations *ab extra*. Sometimes the power was ascribed to an unconsciously personified Nature which selected the fit and rejected the unfit. Sometimes the power was conceived as a 'blind material force', similar to that which produces earthquakes or tornadoes. In both cases, misleading conclusions were derived from the metaphor.

We now recognize (or should recognize) that 'natural selection' is not the name of a power or force which impresses itself on populations from the outside, but is a way of designating a complex process which goes on *within* an evolving population. The process, as we have seen, has a negative and a positive side. The negative side is the gradual elimination from the population of certain types of genetic constitution. The positive side involves the building up of certain other types of genetic constitution and their systematic spread through the population. In this activity there is a maintaining and improving of the adaptations of individual carriers of the genotypes; or the determining of new modes of adaptation to new environmental conditions. No 'external' power comes into play here. What happens is wholly immanent to the complex situation in which a population interacts with its environment.

There can be no objection, of course, to speaking of selection as a power, if by this we merely wish to stress its causal efficacy within an evolving population. It is convenient and natural to say that selection 'produces' effects, and this mode of speech readily suggests the idea of an active force at work. But the suggestion will not lead to difficulties provided we keep in mind what is actually going on.

'*Natural Selection as Creative.*' Some biologists have adopted the practice of calling selection a 'creative' factor in evolution. This expression has, however, such a variety of meanings that the appropriateness of its use in connection with selection is not immediately obvious. I will conclude the present section by making a few remarks on the issues involved here.

In order to avoid opening up too large a topic, I will limit my discussion to cases where 'creative' is applied to a process which results in the production of things or substantial entities, not qualities and relations. With this limitation, it is possible to distinguish at least three senses of the expression relevant to natural selection.

(α) A process may be described as 'creative' if by means of it something springs into existence, yet does not then become a further stage of the history of anything that was already there. What is thus created either remains isolated or is the start of a new strand of history. Hence, it is not produced from pre-existing material or 'stuff'. This can be called 'pure' or 'absolute' creation (Cf. Broad, 1923, 536). Traditional Christian theology regards the Divine act by which the universe was brought into being *ex nihilo* as 'creative' in this sense. Some recent cosmological theories have likewise postulated a creation *ex nihilo* of matter, and have even specified the rate at which such creation takes place (Bondi, 1952, 143).

(β) A process may be described as 'creative' if by means of it something which did not previously exist is brought into existence by rearranging bits of material already there. What is produced is analysable without loss into these bits of material together with the relations in which they are combined. Thus a boy 'creates' a model out of the parts of a Meccano set, and later reverses the process by dismantling his creation into its components. This type of productive activity might be called 'mechanistic creation'. It is in principle reversible, and its products are mechanical systems.

(γ) There are cases where something is brought into being out of pre-existing material, but where what is produced cannot be analysed without loss into bits of the material and their combining relations. Moreover, this process is not in principle reversible. Thus, a painter creates a picture by mixing and utilizing his pigments in various ways; or the sculptor creates a statue by carving a block of marble. What results is an artistic whole or 'system' quite different from a mechanical aggregation of parts. A process which results in the production of such wholes or systems might be called 'organic creation'.

Now natural selection is clearly not 'creative' in sense (α). For it does not generate the material with which it works. This material is provided by genetic processes. Nor is selection plausibly described as 'creative' in sense (β). For its products are almost certainly not mechanical structures which can be fully analysed into a set of component parts and connecting relations. We are therefore left with the meaning of 'creative' specified in (γ). If we agree that selection always gives rise to integrated genetic *systems* which render their carriers viable, we lay a foundation for saying that its activity is creative in the third sense. Furthermore, as various people have pointed out, rather close parallels can be drawn between this activity and the process of artistic creation. Thus, in its negative rôle, 'just as a sculptor creates a statue by removing chips from an amorphous block of marble, so natural selection creates new systems of adaptation to the environment by eliminating all but the favourable gene combinations out of the enormous diversity of random variants which could otherwise exist' (Stebbins, 1950, 104). Similarly, in its positive rôle of determining what gene combinations will survive and how they will be built into organized wholes, natural selection can be regarded as similar in its operation to the activity of a poet who determines what words in what particular combinations will produce the aesthetic whole he desires to create. Such considerations show that selection can be appropriately called 'creative' in the sense specified.

If we speak in this way, however, we should keep in mind that the results of selection do not always appear to be admirable from the human standpoint. We can silence the honorific overtones of the word 'creative' by remembering that the tubercle bacillus, the hookworm and the disease-producing viruses owe their places in the evolutionary scheme to the activity of selection. They were 'created' by it in the sense above outlined. Yet many aspects of their parasitic or lethal behaviour are repugnant to civilized persons. This may, of course, be attributed to a purely subjective bias. But the fact remains that natural selection, as Julian Huxley has remarked, 'though like the mills of God in grinding slowly and grinding small,' has few of the attributes that a civilized religion would call divine. It is efficient in its way—at the price of extreme slowness and extreme cruelty . . . accordingly, its products are just as likely to be aesthetically, morally or intellectually repulsive to us as they are to be attractive' (Huxley, 1942, 485). Hence to say that selection is 'creative' does not imply that whatever it brings into existence has positive or intrinsic value. In this respect it is clearly different from artistic production, just as biological systems are different in important respects from works of art. The use of the expression 'creative' by exponents of modern selectionist theory is, therefore, descriptive, not evaluative. The expression characterizes but neither commends nor condemns.

(v) *Laws and Predictions in Selectionist Theory.* Modern selectionist theory is undoubtedly the most powerful systematic explanation so far devised of recurrent evolutionary phenomena. It also contributes in a fundamental way to explaining the total course of evolution. Its power springs from the fact that it has been able to integrate a number of the causal factors which we have good reason to believe were at work throughout the history of life on the earth. These factors and their inter-relations are specified in generalizations or law-like statements, many of which have been reproduced in the course of the foregoing discussion. Since the presence of the law-like statements is what marks off the explanations as systematic, it will be well to assemble and comment on a representative sample of them. Then something may be said about their predictive efficacy.

The following items constitute the sample:

(1) Every phenotypic character of every organism is controlled by the organism's genotype.
(2) Every genotype is an integrated system.
(3) In every population genetic mutations occur with a certain relative frequency.
(4) The occurrence of a mutation is always undirected or random.
(5) Every enduring population is adapted to the environmental niche in which it lives.
(6) In every population there occurs a process of differential reproduction of the best adapted organisms.
(7) Most phenotypic traits of an organism have adaptive value.
(8) Most viable populations exhibit a trend towards increasing specialization.
(9) Populations which become reproductively isolated usually evolve into distinct species.
(10) Natural selection tends to be more effective in large than in small populations.

Are any or all of the above statements to be regarded as scientific laws? In the light of a recent discussion by Mehlberg (1958, 156ff.), an affirmative answer can be given at least for statements (1)-(7). The form of the statements entitles us to call them 'law-like'; and since a substantial amount of evidence supports them, they can be regarded quite properly as scientific laws. To be sure they do not possess strict universality. They are known to apply only to a limited spatio-temporal region, viz. the earth's surface during some thousand million years. Beyond this region, no objects or events to which they apply have been discovered, although the possibility that such objects and events exist has to be left open. Hence, following Mehlberg, we may say that they are 'regional' or 'vacuously universal' laws. Furthermore, since some of the statements if made quantitatively precise would become statistical, they lack formal universality. Indeed, the great difficulty of formulating *any* biological generalizations to which there are not exceptions might well incline us to regard all law-like statements in evolutionary theory as statistical at bottom. But a statement can still qualify for the title of 'scientific law' even though it fails to have spatio-temporal and formal universality. It does not follow, of course, that any of the above statements should also be called 'laws of nature' (Mehlberg, *ibid.*).

The case of statements (8)-(10) is somewhat different. They are a representative sample of generalizations about 'tendencies' and 'trends' which are found frequently, but by no means always, when certain conditions are fulfilled. The looseness of the statements makes any statistical evaluation of them quite impossible. At best they approximate to the character of scientific laws, and hence might be called 'quasi-laws'. They are statements of limited generality and exactitude, based upon qualitatively assessed evidence. Yet they have a useful explanatory rôle to play within evolutionary theory. It is common for the 'inexact sciences' to contain many such quasi-laws, as recent studies have shown (Cf. Helmer and Rescher, 1959).

The informal indication which has been given of how some of these laws and quasi-laws perform their explanatory function is perhaps enough to suggest that what takes place rarely, if ever, conforms to the simplified deductive model of explanation which applies rather widely in the physical sciences. Consider a particular instance of a recurrent evolutionary phenomenon, say, species formation. We undoubtedly know a number of law-like statements which are relevant to its occurrence. But, as I will argue in the next section, our knowledge is far from complete. Hence, the particular instance cannot be accounted for by *deducing* a statement describing it from an assemblage of factual statements and general laws. This is too simple a model in terms of which to interpret the situation. Selectionist theory is unable to supply a sufficient number of laws of the sort needed to effect a logical deduction. Moreover, since among the generalizations relevant to species formation there are various statistical principles and quasi-laws, any strict derivation or formal entailment of a statement specifying the *explicandum* is precluded.

The proper conclusion seems to be that law-like statements in selectionist theory serve not as premises for deductions but as components in evidential systems which render *explicanda* intelligible or rationally credible. Thus the cluster of statements marshalled to account for a particular instance of species-formation is such that the statements mutually reinforce and sustain one another. They constitute evidential grounds for what is to be explained. The situation can be compared with that of a partially finished crossword puzzle in which various entries interlock and offer each other support. Even though blanks remain to be filled, the result may be virtually conclusive and leave no room for alternative solutions. The objection may be raised that the analogy is imperfect in one crucial respect, namely that whereas all the entries of a crossword puzzle have the same relative importance, the law-like statements of an evidential system are by far its most important items. To this the reply can be made that law-like statements are comparable to those long words in a puzzle which interlock with numerous other and which greatly advance the solution once they are found. But the analogy obviously cannot be pushed too far. The essential point is that a crossword puzzle is a more apt model than a deductive chain in the light of which to understand the explanatory function of selectionist theory (Cf. Rescher, 1958).

To what extent do law-like statements of the kind listed above make predictions possible? In considering this question two untenable extremes can at once be rejected: (a) no scientific predictions of any kind are possible about the future course of evolution; and (b) every detail of the future course of evolution is predictable in principle. Position (a) is untenable because we do have a well-supported theory of evolution containing numerous law-like statements. These constitute a perfectly sound basis for making *some* positive forecasts which are more than just prophecies or wild guesses. On the other hand, (b) is untenable for several reasons. First, it is highly doubtful whether the expression 'predictable in principle' can be given any meaning which will differentiate it from 'predictable in practice' (Cf. O'Connor, 1957). And it is patent that we have in practice no power to predict the details even of a short segment of evolution. Secondly, there is no single, comprehensive 'law of evolution' in the light of which the whole future course of phylogenesis can be plotted. As a unique, historical phenomenon evolution is not the sort of thing which could be thus law-bound (Cf. Popper, 1957b). Thirdly, selectionist theory itself interprets what happens at each stage of evolution as the outcome of the interaction of random genetic occurrences and non-random selective processes. An element of 'chance' is built into the theory. Hence there is no place for the notion of exhaustive predictability, even as a theoretical ideal.

A familiar difficulty connected with this subject is that no clear-cut rules exist for deciding whether a scientific formula should be accounted a prediction or not. We may be tempted to look for rules in the case of spectacularly successful predictions, such as the astronomer's forecasts of eclipses for years ahead. Yet to take these cases as paradigmatic is to overlook the fact that they depend on very special circumstances. Eclipses are subject to long-range forecasts only because the solar system is a relatively isolated, stable and repetitive system. Comparatively few phenomena of this kind occur in nature, and none occur among the items with which an evolutionist is concerned. Certain biological phenomena, to be sure, do have cyclical or repetitive aspects capable of being treated in abstraction from the gradual evolutionary changes to which they are subject. Here predictions akin to those of astronomy are perhaps possible, e.g. in embryology and ecology. But an evolutionist has to deal with organisms and populations undergoing continuous, non-repetitive changes. These organisms and populations are open systems, ceaselessly interacting with the environment and each other. Hence he can hardly hope to produce anything akin to astronomical forecasts. Yet it would be unwarrantable to conclude that he is unable to produce any positive forecasts at all.

This matter may be pursued a little further as follows. An astronomer is able to make unconditional and also conditional predictions about eclipses. Thus he may state that 'a total solar eclipse will occur in region r at time t'; or he may state that 'if factors f_1, f_2, f_3, . . . f_n are present, then a total solar eclipse will occur in region r at time t'. He can make the unconditional prediction because he has at his disposal a complete set of mathematical laws which govern the motion of the sun, moon and earth relative to each other. From these laws, together with information about the actual positions of those bodies at a given time, he can deduce the statement containing the prediction. Similarly, he can make the conditional prediction because factors f_1, f_2, f_3, . . . f_n together imply the predictive statement. This is the well-known situation where symmetry prevails between the logical structure of a prediction and that of a corresponding explanation of a given event after it has occurred. Such symmetry, however, by no means holds 'right across the board' in science (Cf. Scheffler, 1957).

An evolutionist is unable to make forecasts of either of the above types. Not only do the law-like statements which he has available lack a mathematical form, but in no single instance has he a set of them complete enough to serve as a premiss for an unconditional prediction. Because the factors he is able to specify are insufficient to allow a standard 'if . . . then . . . ' proposition to be formulated, a conditional prediction is likewise out of the question. Hence it seems clear that evolutionary forecasts depend on a weaker relation to their supporting grounds than do the forecasts of astronomy. The best an evolutionist can do is to predict in some such terms as: 'if f_1, f_2, f_3, . . . then very likely p', 'if f_1, f_2, f_3, . . . then p will tend to occur rather than r', 'if f_1, f_2, f_3, . . . then in general we may expect p', and so on. As Scriven has pointed out (1959), certain of these may be called 'hypothetical probability predictions'. But certain others scarcely involve even the notion of 'probability', except in a qualitative sense. Only a limited number of evolutionary phenomena, of course, are amenable to predictive treatment.

Some considerations which have a direct bearing on these points will be introduced in the last chapter of the study. I will there take up the question of forecasting the over-all future course of evolution, with special reference to the likelihood of its continuance for an extended period of time. This sort of forecast is bound to be extremely general at best. Hence it illustrates the methodological points noted above less adequately than does a specific, limited prediction concerning particular phenomena. One or two such predictions will therefore be mentioned in concluding the present section.

Suppose a small isolated population, P, consisting of 10^2 interbreeding animals, is discovered. By virtue of a law-like statement which asserts that genetic drift tends to occur in such populations, we can predict that P will probably be poorly adapted and that its chances of avoiding extinction for very long are small. This prediction is far less securely grounded than any astronomical forecast. Yet it is certainly more than just a guess. It has *some* foundation in the available evidence, even though not deducible from any premisses which we are entitled to adopt. Again, suppose we come upon a large population (e.g. 10^5 interbreeding animals) subdivided into many (e.g. 10^3) partially isolated populations of small size (e.g. 10^2 animals). Concerning this total population we can predict a future evolution which will probably be sustained, relatively rapid and progressive. As in the previous case, our prediction depends on the acceptance of a law-like

statement, in this instance a statement about the optimum conditions for evolutionary changes of the kind specified. Yet
what we forecast is conditioned by a large number of factors
(e.g. the future state of the population's environment, its mutation rate, etc), and because of our limited knowledge we cannot
provide anything like a full inventory of them. Hence our prediction must be at best an approximation having a substantial
margin of probable error. So it is with all predictions which
modern selectionist theory makes possible.

4. IS EVOLUTION FULLY EXPLAINED?

A little more light may be shed on the sort of limitations to
which our present knowledge of evolutionary factors is subject,
if we ask whether evolution is fully explained by modern selectionist theory. At first glance it may seem unprofitable to raise
such a question. Surely, many people will say, the answer is
obvious. We all know, or should know, that evolution is far
from being fully explained by any theory. Yet to dismiss the
question in this fashion is hardly satisfactory. It fails to take
advantage of an occasion which may allow us to discover why
a negative answer seems so obvious, and to determine what
degree of completeness modern selectionist theory has actually
achieved. These are the topics to be canvassed in the present
section.

Let me try to outline the state of affairs which would have
to exist if evolution were 'fully explained'. In the light of the
foregoing discussion, we must say that at least the following
would have to be known: (i) the detailed historical course of
evolution; (ii) historical explanations of all those single, non-
recurrent events which were transitional episodes of major significance in (i); (iii) systematic explanations involving generalizations or laws of the various evolutionary patterns or recurrent
events in phylogenesis; and (iv) the precise manner in which
(ii) and (iii) are to be combined in an over-all theory, such that
it will account for (i) regarded as a single, complex historical
process with large-scale features of its own. It is fairly apparent,
even without further analysis, that available knowledge on all
four points is nothing like complete.

With regard to (i), the largest gap in our knowledge occurs
at the beginning of life's history, because of the scarcity of Pre-

Cambrian fossils. This gap may actually embrace as much as three-quarters, and almost certainly embraces half, of the total history of life, for the first living thing existed on the earth at least 1,000 million years ago (probably longer), whereas only since the Cambrian period is the fossil record reasonably adequate. Yet significant blanks in the record occur during the past 500 million years, so that although we know the outlines of the story, we remain ignorant about innumerable details.

Much the same is true of the cases where historical explanations of single events are needed. It cannot be said that for each of these events a possible sufficient condition of the sort described above is available. We are, for instance, unable at present to trace with assurance a temporal sequence of necessary and contributory conditions which will account for the origin of birds from reptilian ancestors. No one has so far been able to offer an acceptable explanation of the extinction of the dinosaurs; and so on. Even in cases where widely accepted historical explanations exist, there remains the question of how far they have been verified, i.e. have been able to withstand attempts to overthrow them on the basis of empirical evidence. This is a question we hardly know how to go about answering.

If we turn to the systematic explanations proposed for recurrent evolutionary phenomena, we meet a logical consideration which must lead us to doubt whether any one of them is known to be 'fully explained'. Let us say that a recurrent phenomenon is fully explained if and only if a theory exists which we know specifies 'the cause' of it. This means (a) that we can formulate in the theory a set of factors (necessary and contributory) which constitutes a sufficient condition of the phenomenon; and (b) that this theory is empirically verified or established with a substantial probability. Now it is in principle more difficult to establish a set of factors as sufficient for any event than to establish each of these factors as necessary for that event. This is true of even a relatively simply, easily isolated and frequently recurrent phenomenon. Take the case where factors ABCD are repeatedly observed to give rise to E; and where the absence of one or more of the factors results in the non-occurrence of E. Under these circumstances we can be reasonably sure (i.e. there is a high probability) that each factor is a necessary condition of E. But we cannot be nearly as sure that the factors are jointly a sufficient condition of E. For there may be at least one other factor which, though unobserved, was present in all cases which came under our notice, and was necessary for the occurrence of E. Hence, 'statements that such and such conditions are jointly sufficient to produce a certain result should . . . always be viewed with suspicion' (Broad, 1923, 500). Even in a simple case, establishing 'the cause' of a phenomenon is an enterprise fraught with difficulties.

These difficulties are vastly increased when the phenomenon is complex and virtually impossible to isolate, as evolutionary phenomena are. In investigating these phenomena, even the establishing of a single factor as necessary requires the adoption of a procedure which cannot ensure uncontroversial results. For we are unable to discover or to set up exactly the sort of situation in which we can directly observe the absence of a relevant causal factor, and then observe the failure of evolution to occur. The best that can be done is to imagine a situation (i.e. to construct a theoretical model) in which a factor is *assumed* to be absent, and then *infer* that evolution *could not* take place, given the absence of that factor. Something very like this procedure has been adopted by most investigators, as the preceding discussion has shown. Yet the diversity of possible models, and the fact that each is a greatly simplified version of what may have taken place, make it hard to arrive at definitive, universally accepted conclusions.

Simpson has given a brief glimpse of the variety of results reached by competent investigators. He notes that for Darwin the factors which can be supposed in sum to account for evolution are: natural selection, the inherited effect of use and disuse, the inherited effects of environmental action on organisms, and spontaneously occurring variations. The French biologist, Cuénot (1951), specifies as certain: variation, environmental action, competition, and selection. He then adds as 'uncertainties': the inheritance of acquired characters and a finalistic or vitalistic factor. The German authority, Rensch (1947), takes the cause of microevolution (and probably also of macroevolution) to be the combined action of mutation, variation in population size, reproductive isolation, and selection. Simpson himself (1953) catalogues the major causal determinants as: variation, differences in population size and structure, mutation, time and length of generations, selection, environmental changes, the interaction of all these factors in adaptation, and isolation

I

and splitting. But he does not contend that this list is exhaustive. Newman (1936) distinguishes five main agencies: heredity (the persistence factor), sex (the diversity-increasing factor), mutation (the change factor), selection (the guiding factor), and isolation (the dividing factor). Other analyses could be cited differing slightly or markedly from each of the above.

It should now be a little clearer why no one in his senses would wish to argue that evolution is fully explained. We cannot fill substantial gaps in the reconstruction of the history of life. Historical explanations of certain transitional episodes in the ascent of life are not available. Great difficulties stand in the way of establishing that a particular set of factors is a sufficient condition of any phenomenon (singular or recurrent). These considerations alone point unmistakably to the conclusion that no complete account of the cause of the evolutionary process as a whole, or any part of it, is possible at present.

What is possible, however, is a partial explanation or partial explanations. There can hardly be any doubt that some of the patterns put forward as historical explanations of singular episodes do succeed in delineating temporal sequences of necessary and contingent contributory conditions, even though no conclusive sufficient condition may be constituted. Hence, it is proper to say that we do know some of 'the causes' of those episodes, without perhaps knowing 'the cause' or 'a cause' of any one of them. Likewise, there can hardly be any doubt that modern selectionist theory has succeeded in locating a number of the necessary conditions of recurrent patterns in evolution as well as of the total evolutionary process. Neither the patterns nor the process would have occurred in the absence of genetic mutations, environmental changes, reproductive isolation, variation in population size, natural selection, etc. Each of these factors is appropriately described as 'a cause', and two or more of them as 'causes' of evolution. Phylogenesis is, therefore, partially explained because there exists a well-grounded theory which formulates some—indeed, the most important—of its causes.

This is actually the view which seems implicit in many biological discussions. When biologists refer to the 'factors', 'forces', 'determinants', etc, of evolutionary phenomena, especially of evolutionary changes, the context suggests that what they have in mind are certain necessary conditions only, i.e. conditions whose absence would have made it impossible for the *de facto* course of evolution to have happened. Perhaps no biologists would care to assert that we know *all* these necessary conditions. But there would be considerable support for the assertion that we know the major ones. We may not have reached a 'full explanation', but a solid start has been made on the road towards it.

The main conclusion of this section, as far as modern selectionist theory is concerned, is one which certain biologists have arrived at on other grounds. Thus, Rostand and Waddington, who reject vitalism, finalism and Neo-lamarckism, are of the opinion that modern selectionist theory has not given a completely satisfactory account of adaption. Waddington (1953, 187) asks: 'Is it really sufficient to suppose that the extraordinarily precise fitting of an animal into its ecological niche is due solely to the selection of random variations?' His answer tends to be in the negative. Rostand likewise affirms: 'Nous conviendrons que l'adaptation organique, dans son ensemble, attend encore une explication exhaustive. Malgré l'imposant appareil mathématique de la Génétique évolutive, . . . nous doutons que la sélection naturelle ait pu, même avec les immenses durées dont disposa l'évolution, créer des organes aussis complexes que le cerveau, l'oeil, l'oreille de Vertébrés supérieurs' (Rostand, 1951, 198). Both men are equally doubtful whether any available theory can account satisfactorily for 'macro-evolution', i.e. the origin of the higher categories of organisms. Neither the systemic mutations postulated by Goldschmidt nor the cumulative effect of small mutations postulated by modern selectionist theory are deemed to be adequate explanations of macro-evolutionary phenomena. Presumably, then, there must be some undiscovered causal factor or factors operative here. 'At this stage of our knowledge it may be pardonable to be vague about the details of the means by which macro-evolutionary changes may be expected to be brought about. It is clear that unorthodox approaches are needed' (Lerner, 1958, 269).

The embryologist, Dalcq, although sympathetic to the contentions of modern selectionist theory, has pointed out how difficult it is for the theory to account for the fact that the main types of morphogenetic organization have diverged from one or more primary patterns. When a new phylum emerged in evolutionary history, drastic transformations must have taken place in the eggs to allow new kinds of developmental processes to occur. Moreover, these transformations must have been viable from the outset. Dalcq thinks that they could not have been achieved piecemeal by small successive steps, progressively stabilized by natural selection. Hence, he proposes 'the new concept of *onto-mutation* to designate the sudden appearance of a new type of egg organization with all the logical implications necessary to ensure the successful beginning of a new phylum'. But this is admittedly a speculative idea unsupported by any evidence. The idea is only put forward because 'a causal embryologist reaches much the same conclusion as do some of the best students of evolution under its other aspects: some discovery has still to be made to render really intelligible the history of life and of morphogenesis' (Dalcq, 1951, 112-113).

There are, then, both methodological and empirical reasons for concluding that the explanation of evolution is incomplete. This is really not surprising when one remembers how young evolutionary science is. It has succeeded in understanding many of the causal factors at work. But much more will be disclosed by future investigations. For the present, to quote Rostand again, 'S'agissant du problème de l'évolution, comme de tant d'autres, la plus sage attitude, et la plus loyale, est, nous semble-t-il, *de réserver la place d'un inconnu qu'on s'abstiendra de baptiser et dont on se gardera faire un inconnaissable*' (Rostand, 1951, 203).

CHAPTER IV

THE EVOLUTIONARY ACCOUNT OF MAN

---

1. MAN'S PLACE IN THE EVOLUTIONARY PICTURE

No reasonable person acquainted with the evidence can doubt that man is a product of evolution. For although the evidence is fragmentary, it points unmistakably to the conclusion that a long line of descent connects *Homo sapiens* with pre-human ancestors. A century ago this conclusion was vehemently rejected by large numbers of people. Today it is widely accepted, though its far-reaching implications are not always kept in mind. The early followers of Darwin did not attach any special significance to human evolution as such. Man, they declared, is simply one of the animals, and his production was due to precisely the same evolutionary forces which gave rise to all the other organisms. Recent biological discussions, however, have tended to stress the uniqueness of man as a member of the animal kingdom, and have pointed out that his emergence from a pre-human stage involved unusual circumstances. Indeed, the course of his evolution since emerging has been determined by new factors of a non-biological kind. This is another of the departures from classical Darwinism which merits our attention. In the present chapter, we will look at it with a philosophical eye, and try to understand its broad significance.

There is not much disagreement about man's place in the evolutionary picture. *Homo sapiens* is almost certainly the youngest species of mammal now on the earth. His point of origin lies somewhere in the Middle Pleistocene period, approximately a hundred thousand years ago. He is the only surviving species of the genus *Homo*, and his nearest living relatives are the large anthropoid apes. The group known as the *Hominoids* (to which members of the genus *Homo* and the apes belong) seems to have split off from the main primate stem in an adaptive radiation which occurred between ten and twenty million years ago. Only a small number of lines deriving from this radiation have survived; and only a relatively small number of fossil remains of extinct lines have so far been discovered. Hence the detailed reconstruction of the history of the *Hominoids* remains conjectural and controversial. We are still faced with 'the riddle of man's ancestry' (Straus, 1949). Nevertheless, it is fairly well agreed that modern man is a species of recent origin, and that while not deriving from any existing branch of the ape family, he shares with the apes a common ancestor who flourished in the Miocene or perhaps the Oligocene period.

Judged in terms of the geological time-scale, the rise of *Homo sapiens* has taken place with extreme speed. The process is, in fact, an instance of 'quantum evolution', which, as we saw in Chapter II, p. 54, is the somewhat rare process whereby a group of organisms moves *en masse* into a new adaptive zone, takes on a new way of life, and, as a consequence, undergoes major changes of form and function. The rate of evolution in this case is accelerated to a maximum. Furthermore, since quantum evolution involves an 'all or none' reaction on the part of the group, 'transitional forms between the old zone and the new cannot, or at any rate do not, persist. Populations tending towards the new zone are carried fully into it' (Simpson, 1953, 389). The rapidity of man's evolution may be the chief reason why the fossil record of his ancestry is so meagre.

Although *Homo sapiens* originated some 100,000 years ago, the group which he formed remained a small, relatively insignificant one for more than half of that time. 'Then, towards the very end of the last Ice Age, the human deployment really began, as a major process of expansion which turned man from an unimportant minor branch into a new dominant group' (Huxley, 1953, 57). During the last fifty thousand years, various subgroups of the human species passed from the stage of savagery through the stages of barbarism to civilization. But it is only during the last five or six thousand years—approximately 5 per cent of the whole period of his terrestrial existence—that man has lived in any sort of civilized condition. Viewed in the light of the total evolutionary process modern man is a veritable new-born babe who has just appeared on the scene.

Since *Homo sapiens* is the latest species of mammal to emerge, there is a sense in which he is quite literally the highest species. For in stratigraphical geology, 'later than' implies 'higher up than' in an undisturbed sequence of sedimentary deposits. Hence any fossil remains of man would have to occur in the topmost strata, above the fossil remains of all other species (Child, 1941; 1951). It does not follow that this is the *only* sense in which he is the highest form of life thus far; but it is one perfectly evident sense. Rather more controversial is the contention that man is a 'dominant' form of life on the earth at present. To elucidate the meaning of this contention, we must look briefly at the context in which it has been put forward.

Paleontologists are agreed that evolutionary history is divisible into a succession of 'ages', each bearing the name of a type of life. General agreement also exists about the order in which the ages followed one another and about their correlation with geological eras or periods. Thus the Cambrian period is called the 'age of invertebrates'. It was succeeded by the 'age of fishes', which, in the Mesozoic era, was succeeded by the 'age of reptiles'. Then came the 'age of mammals' in the Tertiary period, and it eventually gave place to the 'age of man'. Each of these titles refers to a particular group of organisms which 'dominated' the age in question. Hence evolutionary history is frequently represented by paleontology as a sequence of 'dominant types'.

What are the distinguishing attributes of a 'dominant type'? The answer to this is by no means clear-cut. But apparently a group of organisms can be described as 'dominant' when (i) its members have a more complex somatic organization than their predecessors in previous ages; (ii) it is numerically more abundant and varied than the other groups in its particular age; and (iii) it has evolved with great rapidity, branching out into a multiplicity of types during the period of dominance. Sometimes the qualification is added that in comparison with previous organisms, a dominant type displays greater ability to deal with the environment in a variety of ways and greater independence of changes going on in its immediate surroundings. Sometimes, too, it is said that a dominant type causes the extinction of other groups of organisms, especially those upon which it preys.

While there seems no reason to doubt the essential correctness of this representation of evolution, its formulation may give rise to misunderstanding if suitable precautions are not taken. For instance, when evolutionary history is said to be 'a succession of dominant types', the impression may be created that there is a single, linear sequence in which one type replaced its immediate predecessor and then was itself replaced, as age followed age.

This impression is erroneous. What it overlooks is that each of the dominant groups rose to its position of pre-eminence by occupying a new environmental niche and becoming a new adaptive type. The reptiles did not become supreme in the same habitat as that of the fishes. The mammals evolved a way of life quite different from that of the reptiles. No simple replacement of one group by another occurred. The model of a linear sequence of dominant types is, therefore, misleading. In other words, 'dominance' does not designate an absolute property of a group of organisms, but a property which is relative to a group's way of life. Accordingly, we should not say of any group that it was 'the dominant form' at a given time, unless we add the rider 'in such-and-such a habitat or way of life'. So formulated, the paleontological succession stands in a much clearer light.

It follows a fortiori that Homo sapiens should be described as 'a dominant', not as 'the dominant' type of living thing now on the earth. Moreover, this dominance is restricted to the sphere of those organisms with whom he can be significantly compared, viz. the hominoids, or perhaps the primates. He cannot be significantly compared with members of other groups in the animal kingdom—such as insects, molluscs, rodents, etc—which are also 'dominant' in their respective spheres, because his mode of life is so different from theirs. Within the primate order, however, man belongs to an evolutionary sequence in which 'he has recently and decisively risen to dominance' (Simpson, 1949, 248). The basis for this judgment lies partly in the fact that Homo sapiens exhibits the attributes of dominant types mentioned above, and partly, no doubt, in the fact 'that man's particular adaptive type was the latest to be developed up to now in the history of life, one radically new, never before exemplified, and with extreme potentialities for expansion' (Simpson, 1949, 248). In the process of expanding, man moved into an environment which no living thing had hitherto occupied. Moreover, as we shall see, there is a sense in which man creates this environment as he evolves, and is now engaged in a struggle to master it. Thus, like the step taken by amphibia and reptiles, which made possible the extension of animal life from the water to the land, so the step taken by the human offshoot of the primate order opened up momentous evolutionary possibilities.

When it is contended that man occupies a pre-eminent place in the organic world, some people, including some biologists, become annoyed. This contention, they declare, is simply a piece of human conceit, a gratuitous move on the part of one member of the animal kingdom to make himself important. Man first constructs an evolutionary ladder, and then puts himself on the top rung. He thereby falls victim to a delusion of his own making, the result of espousing an anthropocentric point of view. An amoeba or an earthworm, if it could express its opinion about evolution, would certainly deny that man stands on the pinnacle of life.

This reaction is a salutary warning against overstating the case for the dominant position of *Homo sapiens*. But a moderate statement of the case based on relevant evidence remains perfectly defensible. For no delusion is involved in the contention that *Homo sapiens* has, during his brief span of existence on earth, evolved with great speed from a place of insignificance to one of prominence among the primates. This is a verifiable contention. Equally verifiable is the contention that man is a new adaptive type possessing an unprecedented power of mastering his environment. He is numerically more abundant, more varied, and more widely distributed over the earth's surface than any other primate species. All these features are certified by evidence. It is futile to indulge in counter-factual speculations about the evolutionary opinions of protozoa or earthworms. For the fact is that *man* is the only living thing who is *able* to formulate a theory of evolution—or any other theory, for that matter. Moreover, when he is considering his own place in the evolutionary picture, an 'anthropocentric point of view' is not only unavoidable but mandatory. The really crucial question is whether his conclusions are based on evidence or not. And since the evidence for man's dominance among the primates is a matter of record, the conclusions he draws are entirely warranted.

It may be objected that this reply does not meet the difficulty. For after all, man's specification of the criteria of dominance is an arbitrary affair. He singles out certain biological characteristics, and decides that they will constitute the basis for defining a 'dominant group'. Then, finding these characteristics exemplified by *Homo sapiens*, he announces that man is the dominant species among the primates. This announcement sounds like the report of a discovery, whereas it is actually the result of an arbitrary fiat.

The appropriate retort to this objection is that it misrepresents an accepted linguistic procedure of science by employing the pejorative expression 'arbitrary'. In every empirical science, there are certain semantic rules which govern the application of words and sentences to non-linguistic phenomena (objects, events, persons, etc). These semantic rules are usually not stated explicitly unless the scientific language is formally described, and then they appear in the metalanguage by means of which the formal description is carried out. Now when a technical word is coined to designate some non-linguistic phenomenon, or when a word (such as 'dominant') is taken over from ordinary speech and used to designate the phenomenon, a new semantic rule is required. Otherwise, the range of application of the word will be unspecified. The formulating or the implicit adoption of a new rule is, of course, a human decision; but it is pointless to speak of the decision as 'arbitrary', for *there is no other or better way of arriving at semantic rules*. All such rules are human productions and cannot be anything else. Accordingly, the above procedure of determining the range of applicability of the expression 'dominant group' by specifying certain criteria which collectively establish a rule for its use, is the only procedure possible. In the present context, the procedure shows clearly the sense in which it is true to say that *Homo sapiens* is a dominant species.

2. THE BIOLOGICAL UNIQUENESS OF MAN

Like every other living thing, man has been moulded by the forces of evolution. His body displays many signs of the long history which lies behind him and of the complex affinities which he has with the rest of the animal kingdom. Yet it is also the case that he possesses a variety of characters *not* shared by any other animal. These characters, or at any rate certain of them, mark him off as a highly unusual member of the living world. Man exhibits a biological uniqueness directly related to his rise to a position of dominance in the evolutionary picture. We must next consider wherein this biological uniqueness consists.

Of central importance is the fact that man has a large, plastic brain capable of an amazing degree of complexity in its functioning. The development of this organ played a vital rôle in the evolution of the whole primate order, conferring an adaptive advantage on its possessors and hence being favoured by natural selection. Indeed, 'increase in size of the cerebrum, increase in relative extent of the neopallium, and increase in its surface by convolution have all occurred in varying degrees in the evolution of most groups of mammals. All three are carried to an extreme in man' (Simpson, Pittendrigh and Tiffany, 1957, 215). Furthermore, there has occurred 'the development of a motor speech-centre in the brain. This region of Broca, a positively allometric brain-region, could be used for a new function' (Rensch, 1954, 198). Some have considered that man's large brain is an abnormality to which he may owe a spectacular short-term success, but which in so young a species is an ominous sign presaging an early evolutionary end. All students are agreed, however, that the character of his brain makes man at present unique among living things.

Around this central feature a number of other unique characters are clustered. There is, for example, the variegated pattern of man's psychical life; his capacity to use spoken and written languages, his capacity for conceptual thought, his impulse towards the artistic expression of his feelings and emotions, his ingenuity and willingness to try experiments. Man is the most adaptable of evolution's creatures (Darwin, 1953). His adaptability is enhanced by the ability to invent and use tools, instruments and machines. This ability in turn is dependent on the possession of hands which can manipulate objects with great skill and efficiency. Man is both Homo faber and Homo sapiens. Each of these functions has interacted with and stimulated the development of the other. But neither would have amounted to much if the human cerebral hemispheres had not evolved to their present state.

Several characters connected with the generation and rearing of offspring differentiate man from the other animals. He has, for instance, high reproductive efficiency, 'the highest in the animal kingdom' (Simpson, 1945, 285). Since he has no breeding season or sexual cycle, the adult human possesses under normal circumstances a reproductive capacity which is continuous over a large part of his life. This continuity in sexual activity contrasts with the sexual periodicity of the vast majority of animals, and has had an important determining effect on various social institutions such as the family. Furthermore, because of his reproductive efficiency Homo sapiens has been able to increase his numbers at an ever-expanding (at the moment, a frightening) rate, and to spread over the habitable surface of the globe.

Even more significant, perhaps, is the slow rate of man's

development from birth to adulthood. Almost one quarter of the average human life-span is required to attain reproductive maturity, and rather more to attain maximum growth. Most animals require far less of their average life-span to reach maturity. The significance of this prolonged pre-adult period is that it gives each individual the time to learn the enormous variety of skills and to master some of the knowledge which he needs to get along in society. 'If men and women were, like mice, confronted with the problems of adult life after a few weeks, or even like whales, after two years, they would never acquire the skills of body and mind that they now absorb from and contribute to the social heritage of the species' (Huxley, 1932, 13). This protracted learning period has an important bearing on the new sort of evolution which man has undergone, as will appear below.

Two final respects in which man's biological uniqueness is shown may be mentioned.

(A) He is the most variable wild species now on the earth, being rivalled only by certain domesticated animals such as the dog and the horse. Haldane (1949) has expressed this fact by saying that man is the most 'polymorphic' and 'polytypic' of the mammals. A species is polymorphic when in the same region there are several different types breeding together, their differences being genetically determined. A species is polytypic when it has different types in different areas. Human polymorphism probably includes innate, psychic traits and abilities as well as purely physical ones. Much of the success of Homo sapiens as a species has probably been due to his psychological polymorphism. Yet mankind has remained a single, reproductively homogeneous population. Hence a profound biological unity underlies all racial diversity. Man's great variability does not prevent him from constituting one species.

(B) Among the somatic traits of Homo sapiens are some which have a special interest because of an interpretation given them by Bolk (1926). He pointed out that adult man has a number of traits which closely resemble the embryonic or foetal characteristics of apes. Typical examples are: a relatively high brain weight, the angle which the head makes with the trunk, the retarded closing of the sutures of the skull, the absence of a complete clothing of hair, the light colour of the skin, etc. It is as though man were a kind of 'pre-natal ape' who has acquired the power of reproduction. Bolk called this phenomenon 'foetalization', and suggested that it marked a process by which the *Hominidean* line was rejuvenated and given fresh evolutionary vigour. This ingenious speculation has not been universally accepted. But there is general agreement that Bolk has called attention to a significant phenomenon. Moreover, it would seem that man's extraordinary foetalization is a special case of the broader phenomenon of neoteny, i.e. the state of affairs in which, because of the retarded development of certain traits, the adult form of an animal resembles the juvenile form of its presumed ancestors. Now neoteny is admitted to have played a part in other phases of phylogenesis. Hence it seems likely to have done so in the case of man. Bolk is thus justified in attributing evolutionary significance to the facts which he was the first to emphasize.

3. MAN'S UNIQUE EVOLUTION

Our previous discussion of the concept of a population and of the continuity of evolution should convince us that it is impossible to say *precisely* where and when *Homo sapiens* arose. We cannot pin-point his origin in space and time, because this was not an individual but a statistical phenomenon, not a discrete event but a continuous process. The temptation may be strong to imagine a primordial Adam to whom the expression 'the first *Homo sapiens*' applied. However, once we realize that this expression no more applies to a particular individual than do the expressions 'the average man' or 'the first proper fraction', we can (perhaps) escape the temptation. The most we can assert at present is that modern man arose during the Middle Pleistocene period, probably on the continents of Asia or Africa. Future investigation may permit the vagueness of this assertion to be reduced. But it can never be stated with perfect precision.

Just as we cannot say exactly where and when *Homo sapiens* arose, so we cannot specify the precise circumstances under which he emerged from pre-human ancestors. In the absence of evidence to the contrary, it is reasonable to assume that the process which led up to him followed the same general pattern as that which prevailed elsewhere among the mammals. In other words, the history of the *Hominoids* may be regarded as a fairly typical example of biological evolution. Until *Homo sapiens* began to emerge, only those causal factors which had been operative in evolution from its beginning were at work. But then an extremely important turn of events occurred. Man himself began to produce a new set of causal factors, and thereby initiated a new kind of evolution. These factors are referred to collectively by the term *culture,* and the new process which they set in motion is called *cultural evolution.* A few of the philosophically interesting aspects of this large subject will now be considered.

The phenomena designated by the term *culture* can be divided into three groups, each connected with certain human capacities. (i) There are the crafts, skills, productive techniques, etc, which reflect man's capacity to invent and use tools and machines. Here is to be found the multifarious handiwork of *Homo faber.* (ii) There are the sciences, the fine arts, the literature, the philosophy, the moral codes, and the religious beliefs, which reflect man's intellectual and linguistic capacities, his creative impulses, and his spiritual ideals. These are the most distinctive products of *Homo sapiens.* (iii) There are the habits, customs, institutions, legal and governmental organizations, etc, which arise from man's need to live in societies. They are the work of *Homo socialis.* Obviously, extensive interaction takes place among the three groups. And every culture exhibits great differences from the rest in the degree of complexity characteristic of its technological, psychical and social dimensions.

A striking way of envisaging all this has been suggested by Teilhard de Chardin (1956; 1955-1957). He proposes an extension of a model often employed by geologists, according to which the earth can be represented by a sequence of concentric, spherical shells—barysphere, lithosphere, atmosphere, and biosphere. The last of these, introduced by the geologist Suess, was intended to represent 'the frail but superactive film of highly complex, self-reproducing matter spread around the world . . . a special planetary envelope of the organic, distinct from the inorganic lithosphere.' Teilhard proposes to say that with the appearance of man an additional planetary 'envelope' came into being. He calls it the *noösphere,* 'that marvellous sheet of humanized and socialized matter which, despite its incredible small mass and its incredible thinness, has to be regarded positively as the most sharply individualized and the most specifically distinct of all the planetary units so far recognized' (Teilhard, 1956, 103). The name suggested conveys through its etymology the pre-eminent rôle played in this sphere by rational thought.

At least two different interpretations of the concept of the noösphere have been given. Teilhard uses the concept to refer to the *ensemble* composed of man and his various cultures. The 'marvellous sheet of humanized and socialized matter' includes *Homo sapiens* as its central constituent. It has come into being because man has produced culture and by producing it has transformed himself. Another way interpreting the concept is due to Huxley. He limits its reference to the psychical dimension of culture. This dimension is affirmed to be man's distinctive environment, the *milieu* in which he characteristically lives. 'As fish swim in the sea and birds fly through the air, so we think and feel our way through this collective mental world . . . the noösphere or world of mind' (Huxley, 1953, 110). Here *Homo sapiens* is not a constituent part of the noösphere, but an occupant of it. Both interpretations are defensible as models, though Teilhard's may have certain advantages from a comprehensive point of view.

Within the noösphere the unique process of human evolution has taken place. Strictly speaking, 'human evolution is a singular product of interaction between biology and culture' (Dobzhansky, 1956, 28). For modern man has not ceased to be subject to the biological factors which were responsible for his emergence. These factors are still at work. But they are now less influential in determining his history than are cultural factors. Hence it is customary to refer to what *Homo sapiens* has initiated as *cultural evolution*. This has not replaced but includes biological evolution in a more complex process with various novel features. I will single out three of these features for special comment (Cf. Teilhard, 1956).

(a) There are countless cases in evolutionary history where members of a population have responded to the exigencies of a changing environment by developing organs needed to effect a new adaptation. Often these organs are extremely elaborate. While not extra-somatic, they are comparable with the tools invented by man to solve various practical problems. Cuénot (1941) has argued forcibly that this comparison is not just a vague analogy. There is a close empirical similarity, according to him, between many adaptive organs at the pre-human level and the 'inventions' which have characterized the technological dimension of human culture. If so, it seems appropriate to say that a remarkable degree of 'inventiveness' has been shown by organisms since the beginning of life. They have solved numerous problems of adaptation successfully. Yet, as far as we can tell, this inventiveness was, prior to the emergence of man, entirely unpremeditated. Organisms simply improvised with whatever materials happened to be available at the time.

Cultural evolution, on the other hand, has brought into existence a new form of inventiveness. This is the result of man's ability to devise and execute plans for the realization of his purposes. These purposes are consciously entertained, often, as long-range objectives. The devising of plans calls upon the power of rational thought and constructive imagination. Their execution calls upon theoretical knowledge and technology. Moreover, this new form of inventiveness is far more efficient than the old. It has made possible large-scale control of the physical environment with a minimum of wastage. It works at a speed incomparably faster than anything found in purely biological evolution. During the last century, socially organized programmes of research have been responsible for accelerating the production of inventions at a staggering rate. 'The greatest invention of the nineteenth century was the invention of the method of invention' (Whitehead, 1929, 141). The consequences of all this have not been uniformly advantageous to man, at least on a short-range estimate. There are some who argue that the disadvantages so outweigh the benefits as to constitute another sign that man is approaching the end of his evolutionary trail. Even if those who argue in this way are right, it is still true that the new form of inventiveness resulting from the injection of conscious purposes and plans into evolution, has opened a new (though perhaps short-lived) era in the history of terrestrial life.

(b) The long course of phylogenesis from the first living things to the first representatives of *Homo sapiens* was dependent on the mechanisms of physical heredity. The genetic factors reviewed in the preceding chapter were a necessary condition of evolution. Furthermore, in view of the large-scale features of the evolutionary process mentioned in Chapter II, pp. 38-42—especially the steadily increasing number, diversity, complexity and efficiency of organisms—we seem entitled to say that physical heredity has proved its aptness to promote the ascent of life through various pre-human stages. The inventiveness shown by biological evolution was made possible by the supply of 'raw material' which the genetic factors never failed to provide.

Yet from the standpoint of human evolution, physical heredity has certain limitations. In the first place, its vehicles, the chromosomes and genes, have to pass from each generation to the next along the one channel provided by the sex cells. The smallness of these cells and the fact that in embryogenesis each developmental system can function in only a few possible ways, impose restrictions on the range of potentialities that are transmissible. Inheritance of potentialities proceeds always on single lines from parents to offspring. There is no 'lateral spreading' to other members of the same generation. In addition, physical heredity is conservative and slow to change. When new elements do arise as mutations, they are not elicited by the needs or desires of individuals. Once in existence, these elements exert their effects automatically, and organisms have no control over their modes of functioning. Furthermore, natural selection operates only with reference to the present, eliminating unfit mutations and stabilizing favourable ones in a population. This whole process is 'tedious, difficult and often wasteful' (Huxley, 1951, 606). Finally, the mechanism of physical heredity has the limitation of not allowing any characters acquired by individual members of a population to be transmitted to subsequent generations. The mechanism is therefore incapable of promoting cultural evolution which depends on the transmission of just such characters.

There has appeared within the noösphere a new kind of heredity freed from the above limitations. Thanks to man's psychical capacities—particularly to his high learning ability and his power of using language—a complex cultural legacy has grown up. This legacy is transmitted in some degree to each individual from his birth onwards. Because of the long pre-adult period through which he passes, he is able to learn at least the rudiments of the legacy, and will normally be involved later in teaching them to other individuals. He will also, very likely, make some contributions of his own to the way of life of his community. Here, then, is a new kind of heredity which is cultural or, in the broadest sense, educational.

Unlike physical heredity, this new kind is not restricted to a single channel but is conveyed to individuals in myriad ways. 'Transmission and acquisition of culture occurs by conditioning, teaching, guidance, precept, indoctrination, learning, imitation, and finally by conscious choice. Cultural traits can be transmitted

K

potentially to any number of persons regardless of descent relationships' (Dobzhansky, 1956, 33). New elements arise not 'blindly' as do genetic mutations, but consciously, as thoughts or ideas in individual minds. These ideas often reflect personal or social needs; and once in existence, they are continuously subject to human direction and control. The process of cultural change can therefore be far less 'tedious, difficult and wasteful' than the process of genetic change.

Language is the chief vehicle by which cultural heredity is disseminated. It is so different from the vehicle of physical heredity that any comparison of the two is likely to seem far-fetched. Nevertheless, there is perhaps some point in saying that with regard to flexibility, responsiveness to environmental nuances, and the power to convey an immense range of items, language is immeasurably superior to genes and chromosomes. When used in a responsible way, it is admirably adapted, as they are not, to the storing of knowledge which can become available to peoples remote from one another in space or time. The transmission of all phases of culture is more rapid than anything which can be achieved by genetic factors. In short, 'an incomparably more sensitive and receptive educational heredity is now at work in the noösphere. This is precisely the power needed to collect the over-abundant products and to feed the constantly accelerated progress of a self-evolving process' (Teilhard, 1956, 109).

Although it is essential to underline the differences between physical and cultural heredity, we should not forget that the two inevitably interact. Examples of this interaction are easy to adduce. Thus, the human sexual instinct is genetically determined, but its expression is governed by an intricate array of cultural factors. Similarly, the ability to use language has its basis in the human genotype; yet a man's mother tongue depends on the society in which he was reared. The phenomenon of language, indeed, illustrates another point worth remembering, namely that cultural heredity seems to be found in a primitive form among pre-human animals. We know, for instance, that honey bees employ a 'language' involving symbols of considerable complexity. Ants, termites and other insects establish highly organized social communities. There is evidence of the rudiments of reflective thought, including an impulse of 'pure curiosity', among monkeys and apes. Hence, while cultural heredity exists in a fully developed state only at the human level, it did not come into being *ex nihilo*. Moreover, its earliest manifestations must have had some adaptive value, and have been favoured by natural selection.

(c) The third novel feature of cultural evolution relates to the process of speciation. As already indicated, when an animal population endures for a long period (i.e. not less than half a million years), it tends to split up into branching systems of sub-groups or varieties. Ecological differentiation and reproductive isolation result in some of these varieties becoming new species. This process is normally a gradual one which occurs under the statistical effect of genetic mutations. It leads to a continual increase in the diversity of living things.

The biological history of mankind has not exhibited this pattern. Huxley has expressed the matter by saying that whereas the evolution of most animals has been branching, the evolution of man has been reticulate. In the case of the human family, 'after incipient divergence, the branches have come together again, and have generated new diversity from their Mendelian recombinations, this process being repeated until the course of human descent is like a network' (Huxley, 1941, 6). Thus despite his geographical distribution over the whole planetary surface, man has continued to be a single species, a population combining an exceptional degree of diversity with a unity of biological structure. Within the noösphere, then, there has been no proper zoological speciation.

At the same time, as Teilhard has persuasively argued, there has occurred another sort of branching, which has resulted in the formation of the different human cultures. These cultures may be regarded as constituting for the noösphere the equivalent and the true successors of zoological species in the biosphere. 'Fundamentally . . . culturation is nothing but a "hominized" form of speciation' (Teilhard, 1956, 109). Moreover, this hominized form of speciation opens up possibilities for human evolution which zoological speciation could not provide. At the biological level, a species as it begins to emerge becomes more and more isolated from surrounding species. It shows an increasing impermeability to them, so that it follows its own, quite separate, course of development. Cultures, on the other hand, show a high permeability. They influence, fuse with, and even absorb one another. Planned inventions and techniques, scientific and philosophical ideas, moral and religious beliefs, legal and political practices, etc, readily cross cultural boundaries. This is the process known as 'acculturation'. Its occurrence makes possible the achievement in the noösphere of a kind of integration unknown in the biosphere. The limit to which the process can approximate is a single world-culture in which man's biological unity would be matched by a spiritual unity, a harmonious integration of diverse elements.

The uniqueness of human evolution, then, consists *inter alia* in the fact that it has been subject to a new type of inventiveness, a new type of heredity and a new type of speciation. These features largely account for man's rise to a position of dominance in the living world, a position so distinctive it is little wonder that pre-evolutionary thinkers regarded him as specially created with all his powers fully developed. The new features of his evolution have given *Homo sapiens* not only an unprecedented control over the physical world, but also the capacity (as yet largely inchoate) of controlling in some measure his own further development. Man alone among living things knows that he has evolved. Man alone is able to decide what direction or directions he desires his own future evolution to follow, and can set about acquiring the knowledge he needs to achieve the desired results.

This last consideration points to another facet of the human situation which must be mentioned. Although reflective thought is probably the most potent single factor in the noösphere, another factor has run it a close second, especially during the last five or ten thousand years. This is man's capacity to evaluate his own conduct and to guide it in the light of moral ideals. If we attempt to reconstruct the psychical life of the first representatives of *Homo sapiens*, it is fairly safe to conclude that just as they had only a rudimentary control of their physical surroundings, so they had no more than a rudimentary capacity to make moral judgments about their behaviour. During the millenia between the Pleistocene period and the present, there took place a gradual evolution of the latter capacity, which culminated in what Breasted has called 'the dawn of conscience'. Man's 'moral sense' began to operate more and more in his individual and corporate life. *Homo sapiens* became also *Homo moralis*. If he is ever effectively to control his own evolution, moral ideals or values will have to play a central part in determining its direction. But the relation between evolution and ethics is too big a topic to be explored in the present study.

One other feature of man's evolution is that it is almost certainly incomplete. Several converging lines of thought support this view. For one thing, it is most unlikely that he has arrived at the end of his evolution in the relatively short time he has been on the earth. Throughout pre-human history, anywhere from half a million to a million years have been needed to produce a true species. But Homo sapiens, as we have seen, is only about 100,000 years old. Hence even allowing for the extreme rapidity of his evolution, it is difficult to believe that it has run its course so soon. Furthermore, there is evidence that bodily changes are still occurring in him. He continues to be somatically plastic and subject to the influence of genetic and selectional processes (Cf. Hrdlicka, 1942). With regard to his psychical powers, no great effort of thought is required to arrive at the conclusion that they are only partially developed. 'Man of today is probably an extremely primitive and imperfect type of rational being' (Haldane, 1932a, 153). He is also a primitive type of moral being. Much of his personal and social behaviour exhibits traces of his animal ancestry, just as his physical body does. Yet occasionally he exhibits the power to make his actions conform to the highest moral ideals. For the most part he is indifferent to beauty. Yet he can catch fleeting glimpses of it and embody them in artistic form. Because of all this, the verdict must surely be that man is still in the making. Biologically, he is an adolescent being and does not yet have a fully developed set of *human* traits.

4. HUMAN AND PRE-HUMAN EVOLUTION

Even a brief survey of the human aspect of evolution will place matters in a misleading light if it underlines too heavily the uniqueness of man. Undoubtedly he *does* possess a great number of characteristics not found among any other animals. Undoubtedly his evolution *has* been different in kind from anything which happened on the earth prior to his emergence. Nevertheless, there are certain large affinities between human and pre-human evolution whose significance should not be minimized. I will conclude this chapter by making some comments on them.

Looked at broadly, human and pre-human evolution can be described as processes of self-generated change. What goes on in each case is a 'self-transforming' activity. For both cases involve populations interacting with the environment and thereby *changing themselves.* At the pre-human level, a slow transformation of successive generations of a population takes place in which genetic factors together with their correlated phenotypic characters are altered. Differential reproduction and survival lead to the preservation or spread of certain genotypes at the expense of others. The environment in relation to which this process takes place is, of course, exclusively bio-physical. At the human level, the self-generated change is predominantly cultural and only to a minor extent biological. Gradual transformations take place in man's way of life as a result of his interaction with his cultural environment. There occurs a differential survival of skills, techniques, ideas, beliefs, customs, institutions, etc. New technological, psychical and social factors slowly replace old ones as man makes himself. It is scarcely necessary to add that the replacement of the old by the new is a highly uneven affair in which many cases of 'cultural lag' can be observed.

Throughout pre-human evolution the majority of characteristics of viable organisms have possessed adaptive value. So have the physical products of their genetically controlled, instinctive activities. The webs of spiders, the nests of birds and ants, the dams of beavers, etc, are devices evolved to promote survival in diverse habitats. The same would seem to be true of the products which make up human culture. Before man's ancestor acquired the rudiments of culture, i.e. before he could make tools, control fire, domesticate animals and employ true speech, he was merely one of the beasts, dependent for adaptation on slow evolutionary changes in his body. Since the emergence of *Homo sapiens*, no people has existed without culture; nor, indeed, could any people do so. Culture has, therefore, profound adaptive value. It has even been described as 'the most powerful method of adaptation to the environment ever developed by any species' (Dobzhansky, 1956, 121).

The extent to which the evolution of *Homo sapiens* forms part of one process of terrestrial evolution becomes particularly evident when we take account of man's genetic make-up. For a great many of the constituents of the human gene pool must come from far back in the history of the mammals. These constituents control the development of the mammalian characters manifested in the human phenotype; and they also constitute physical links which connect *Homo sapiens* with the life of the past. Moreover, it was due to these same constituents that man's ancestors were able to reach the stage where cultural evolution could commence. 'Our ancestors were biologically successful precisely because they came to possess the genetic wherewithal to acquire and transmit the rudiments of culture. Because of this adaptive success, the genetic equipment which makes culture possible is being maintained and reinforced by continuous selection going on in most human populations most of the time' (Dobzhansky, 1956, 133). Thus the findings of genetics fully support the view that human and pre-human evolution are interlocking processes.

Man's power of rational thought has often misled him into believing that he stands quite outside the rest of nature. This same power, by enabling him to produce evolutionary science, has given him a more adequate estimate of his position. Although much remains dark, he can at least understand that, despite his uniqueness, he is part of a vast natural process which has gone on since the origin of terrestrial life. This conclusion may well stimulate him to ask further questions; but he cannot reasonably doubt its truth.

CHAPTER V

HAS EVOLUTIONARY THEORY
METAPHYSICAL IMPLICATIONS?

1. PRELIMINARY REMARKS ON THE QUESTION

The preceding chapters have outlined the main features of the theory of evolution now accepted by the majority of biologists. A good deal of the presentation has been concerned with scientific details, although there has also been discussion of logical and linguistic matters at various points. In the present chapter I want to investigate certain issues which arise from reflection on the theory as a whole. These issues are derivable from the question: Has evolutionary theory metaphysical implications? I will begin by making some preliminary remarks about this question. Then I will 'unpack' several of the issues which I believe are contained in it.

The approach to evolutionary theory which has so far been taken might lead the reader to think that the above question can be answered with a simple negative. For I have adopted the view that the theory is a framework of statements having some degree of logical organization, although not of the sort which permits it to be treated axiomatically. The purpose of the framework is to bring order into a mass of empirical data, and to integrate the conclusions of such special sciences as paleontology, comparative anatomy, ecology, embryology, etc. The 'base' of the framework consists of observation-statements which refer directly to empirical data. These observation-statements are the agency by which scientific meaning is conferred on items in the theory, including the large number of statements which contain concepts having no correlates in the perceivable world. Such concepts are required by the historical reconstructions and the historical and systemic explanations which occur at the 'upper levels' of the framework. This well-known, neo-positivistic approach is a fruitful (though restricted) way of considering evolutionary theory. Yet it obviously determines *a priori* that the latter can have no metaphysical implications.

The same result follows from another approach to the theory which is popular among practising biologists. It is clearly put in the following passage.

'The theory of evolution is a biological theory, not a philosophical one. It is a generalization meant to explain the features of organisms of the present and the past by the history of their ancestors and as a result of the action of natural forces within and without the organism in the course of time. . . . The scientist can work only with data which are derived from observation and experiment, and which can be checked, measured, analysed, confirmed and, in the case of experiment, repeated. Thus his work is both factual and pragmatic. . . . If he meets with difficulties, as he invariably will, he hopes for a future solution in the same basic terms, and he works toward that goal. He refuses to take refuge in metaphysics, believing this to be scientific defeatism' (Goldschmidt, 1953, 183-4).

Here evolutionary theory is viewed as an intellectual device which biologists employ, an instrument which is 'factual and pragmatic'. As long as the theory enables them to do the job of ordering, explaining and predicting data of observation, nothing more can be asked of it. New problems which arise are first attacked by using the same instrument which has worked effectively in the past. If it should fail to work, it will be modified and even discarded in favour of another instrument. But the latter will never be a metaphysical doctrine.

The most extreme position which can be taken here is that evolutionary theory has no metaphysical implications because metaphysical utterances generally are devoid of meaning. Underlying this position is the so-called 'verification principle', according to which a statement possesses cognitive meaning only if it is empirically verifiable. It must be confirmable or disconfirmable by sense-experience if it is to have any sense. But metaphysical utterances are such that no possible sense-experiences could confirm or disconfirm them. Consequently, the utterances are cognitively meaningless. The only significant questions and statements about evolution occur *within* biology, or at least within some empirical science.

If any one of the above approaches tells the complete story, then the question being asked in this chapter can be given an immediate, negative answer, and the discussion brought to a close. But, fortunately or unfortunately, there are considerations which must lead us to doubt whether the situation is as simple as this. For it is at least arguable that the complete story is *not* told by the neo-positivistic or the instrumentalist interpretations of evolutionary theory. And it is fairly certain that the extreme position taken by proponents of the verification principle is vulnerable. In short, the question asked at the start of the chapter remains open for discussion, as we may now briefly indicate.

The denial that evolutionary theory has metaphysical implications because the latter are excluded by the verification principle, is one that few people would advance today—although it was popular a decade or more ago. In its heyday, the principle was supposed to be the sword which could slay all metaphysical dragons; but it is now widely agreed that the weapon is defective. No one has been able to offer a satisfactory formulation of the principle, let alone a proof of it (Cf. Hempel, 1951; Mehlberg, 1958). Indeed, serious doubts have been raised about the legitimacy of supposing that *any* principle could be *the* criterion of meaning in the sense that the verification principle purported to be (Cf. Evans, 1953). Metaphysical questions may not allow of being given empirical answers. But this does not establish their 'meaninglessness'. We are left with the possibility that significant metaphysical implications of evolutionary theory can be stated. Yet what sort of statements could they be?

Let us consider in a preliminary way several different replies to this question. It may be argued that neither the neo-positivistic nor the instrumentalist approaches to evolutionary theory does justice to the fact that it can be viewed as a vehicle of *knowledge*. The theory embodies a large measure of the *truth* about living things. This means that the historical reconstructions presented by the theory do describe, with some degree of accuracy, *real* sequences which occurred. The ancient animal and plant forms about which the reconstructions speak *actually existed*. Likewise, historical explanations which have successfully resisted attempts to overthrow them do specify *what is so*. Well-established systematic explanations identify some of the causal factors which determined past evolutionary changes, long before any theory concerning them was propounded. Biologists constantly employ language which shows that they view evolutionary theory in this way as a *cognitive* product. Most of them will probably think that the propositions just stated are so obvious that it is a waste of time to state them. Nevertheless, these propositions are *not part of the framework* of evolutionary theory. They are rather 'metaphysical implications' of it.

This last contention may be supported by pointing out that the italicized expressions above (*knowledge, truth, real, actually existed*, etc) do not represent scientific concepts. They form no part of the vocabulary of evolutionary theory, and biologists do not need them when engaging in their professional activities .Yet biologists can hardly escape interpreting the result of their activities in cognitive terms, and when they do so they need these expressions, or rather, the metaphysical concepts which the expressions represent. Thus a paleontologist not only reconstructs a phylogenetic sequence of, say, the horse family, on the basis of a fragmentary collection of fossils. He believes, and probably says, that the sequence occurred as he has reconstructed it. The members of the long genealogy, from *Eohippus* to *Equus*, actually existed. Indeed, far more individuals existed than will ever figure in any paleontological reconstruction. What he believes and says requires the use of metaphysical concepts.

Part of the intention behind using these concepts is to certify that the reconstruction is not just a bit of science fiction. It is a true account of how things were, or at least a good approximation to the truth about them. Another part of the intention is to ensure that the results of biological activity make sense when considered in relation to the whole scientific enterprise. If the concepts and statements which form the theory of evolution were *merely* a complex apparatus for talking about observable data, so that nothing whatsoever is implied about a real sequence of past events, the theory would not be ultimately intelligible. Its intelligibility therefore depends upon, or 'presupposes', the metaphysical contention that there is an actual evolutionary past which can be scientifically known, but which can never be observed. One sense, then, in which it can be affirmed that evolutionary theory has metaphysical implications arises from the fact that when regarded as a cognitive product the theory implies statements which can only be formulated with the aid of metaphysical concepts.

A slightly different sense in which this same affirmation can be made is related to a point mentioned in Chapter II, pp. 35-6. It was there remarked that the reconstruction of the history of all the populations which have lived on the earth requires the adopting of assumptions in the light of which the empirical evidence is interpreted. The assumption is made, for instance, that certain objects observed to be naturally embedded in the rocks are the remains of animals or plants which were alive in the distant past. A paleontologist requires this assumption because direct observation by itself tells him nothing about the origin of those objects. What he observes is perfectly compatible with a very different assumption, said to have been made by the nineteenth century naturalist, Philip Gosse, that so-called 'fossils' are objects created *in situ* by God when He brought the universe into existence. Their purpose is to test the faith of Christians who might be tempted by the false contentions of Darwinism to doubt the Biblical account of creation.

Why is Gosse's assumption unacceptable to an evolutionist? One reply might be that if it were adopted, no evolutionary theory utilizing fossils as evidence could be advanced. The reconstruction of the history of living things could not get started. Hence the assumption of the special creation of fossils *in situ* is scientifically sterile. It is to be rejected on pragmatic grounds. The evolutionary assumption, on the other hand, is scientifically fruitful. Once we adopt it, a theory can be formulated which accounts for a great deal of other evidence, and makes possible various predictions about future discoveries. This is the position which might be taken by an evolutionist who is thinking only of the instrumental function of his theory.

The majority of evolutionists, however, will probably wish to make another reply. Gosse's assumption, they will say, is unacceptable because it supposes something to be the case which is not the case. The 'assumption' is a false statement. Conversely, the statement that objects called 'fossils' are evolutionary remains affirms what is the case. It is a true statement. We do not assume it so much as *presuppose* it in understanding the theory of evolution. If that theory is a body of knowledge, then what from an instrumental standpoint appears as an assumption, is a presupposition of, though not a proper part of, the theory. And since we need the concept 'true' in order to formulate the presupposition (' "Objects called *fossils* are evolutionary remains" is a true assertion'), we can appropriately speak of the presupposition as 'metaphysical'.

Another example of this kind of thing is the 'uniformitarian principle' alluded to in Chapter III, p. 61. Its function is to make possible the extrapolation backwards in time of results obtained from the investigation of present-day organisms. The principle states, roughly, that factors and laws now discovered to be operative in the biological domain were operative throughout all or most of the history of life. An evolutionist has to espouse this principle if he is to employ the findings of sciences such as genetics to construct systematic explanations of phenomena of the remote past. If he did not espouse it, his theory would fail to work. But again, the situation has to be understood in more than instrumental terms. For the doctrine of evolution would fail to be intelligible unless the uniformitarian principle describes what is the case. It must be true that biological factors and laws now known to be operative were at work in the past. This is a statement incapable of being proved within evolutionary theory, because it functions as a metaphysical presupposition of that theory.

There is a third sense in which an affirmative answer might be given to the question asked at the beginning of the chapter. When speaking professionally, biologists sometimes state that evolution is a single, historical process. From a scientific standpoint, this statement is a high-level abstraction whose empirical meaning is wholly derived from its very indirect connection with what is observable in nature. But when construed metaphysically, the statement is taken to describe a real process which has gone and is going on, quite independently of any theorizing about it. What is described has an existential status in its own right. Now we can appropriately ask whether this real process has an overall *direction*, whether it exemplifies *progress* or *retrogression*, whether it shows signs of *purpose*, whether any special significance is to be attributed to it in virtue of the fact that the process has given rise to *consciousness* or *mental* phenomena, etc. These are metaphysical questions, although they have frequently been raised in the course of ostensibly scientific treatises. To answer them, affirmatively or negatively, is to admit that evolutionary theory has metaphysical implications.

The French biologist, Vandel, has taken a position rather close to the one just outlined. Like many of his countrymen, he holds that an exclusively scientific account of evolution is not enough. 'Reconnaissons très franchement que le problème de l'Evolution déborde largement le cadre scientifique. Vouloir envisager l'Evolution sous le seul angle objectif, ce du même coup la mutiler dangereusement, renoncer à en comprendre les aspects essentiels et en méconnâitre la véritable signification. L'Evolution a des prolongements métaphysiques que nous ne pouvons ignorer' (Vandel, 1949, 50). The chief metaphysical extensions arise when we try to integrate man with the evolutionary process. For then we are bound to raise questions about 'progress' and 'purpose' which are not amenable to scientific treatment, because they involve making evaluations. These evaluations in turn depend upon 'données subjectives et métaphysiques'. We cannot close our eyes to such data and still hope to understand the meaning of evolution.

A fourth approach to this matter may be mentioned to wind up these preliminary remarks. Some people have contended that the conclusions of evolutionary theory have important bearings on the world-picture which we are entitled to accept. A 'world-picture' may be taken to be a more or less coherent set of fundamental beliefs, embodying concepts of maximum generality, about the universe as a whole and man's place in it. For centuries there have been competing world-pictures—materialism, idealism, theism, naturalism, etc—each with its partisans and each held in a vague or an explicit form. All of them are conceded to be metaphysical doctrines.

Now the conclusions of evolutionary theory may affect these doctrines in at least two ways. (A) If the conclusions are true, then certain world-pictures have to be rejected because they conflict with them. The field of competing metaphysical doctrines is thereby narrowed. Furthermore, the truth of the conclusions may give support to some rather than to others of the surviving doctrines. (B) The integrating power of evolutionary conclusions has encouraged the project of constructing a world-picture whose central concept is 'evolution'. The concept has, of course, to be generalized so that it can function in its new rôle. In fact a large-scale conceptual revision has to be undertaken. The evolutionary world-picture is like a map of the cosmos drawn according to a new plan. It incorporates the findings of biological science about the history of life; but it also tries to embrace many other items in a comprehensive, metaphysical scheme. We will glance at one of these schemes in a moment.

The foregoing discussion shows that the question, Has evolutionary theory metaphysical implications?, is not to be given a quick, negative answer. The question needs to be ventilated in more detail by getting down to cases. I propose to examine some of these cases in the remainder of the chapter. The nature of the examination will oblige me to move back and forth between evolutionary theory and the metaphysical issues being discussed, so that a number of scientific details already touched on, and some new ones, will be brought into a philosophical focus.

2. BIOLOGICAL EVOLUTION AND COSMIC EVOLUTION

Darwin's version of evolutionary theory stimulated many persons to extrapolate his central ideas beyond the limits of biology. It was natural to suppose that ideas which were so successful in dealing with living things would be equally successful in dealing with the universe at large. If organisms evolve, why not the cosmos? Spencer was one of the first to carry out such an extrapolation. He regarded the concept of evolution as applicable to matter and motion everywhere. Peirce, likewise, held that 'philosophy requires thorough-going evolutionism or none'; and he himself proposed a cosmological scheme in which not only the material, but also the laws, of the universe have evolved (Peirce, 1931-35, VI, 14). These and other attempts to produce a world-picture by utilizing the concept of evolution might be looked upon as historical curiosities, the result of ambitions which no one today would share. Yet, in fact, just such a world-picture has been put forward by a distinguished exponent of modern evolutionary theory, Julian Huxley. I will take his views to be typical of those who try to connect biological with cosmic evolution.

What Huxley has to say is strongly reminiscent of Spencer. 'Evolution' is regarded as the name of a single, comprehensive process, 'from cosmic star-dust to human society.' The process is in the main continuous; but at certain critical points there is a sudden, rapid passage to new and more complex levels of organization. That which undergoes transformation at all stages is referred to as 'the universal world-stuff' or 'the one ultimate world-substance'. It is not, however, like Spencer's conception of matter and motion, a mere appearance of some unknowable force or power. The world-stuff is reality itself. A more accurate way of putting it might be to say that reality is the ultimate world-stuff undergoing evolution. The process involved is properly considered 'creative' since it both brings new levels of organization into being and also opens up new possibilities of development to the world-stuff.

Two major critical points have so far occurred in this creative process. The first was the transition from non-living matter to life. The second was the transition from pre-human life to man. Consequently, Huxley follows Spencer in distinguishing three main phases of evolution: the inorganic, the biological, and the human or psycho-social. Each of these processes is held to be going on today. But their origins succeeded one another in time. Inorganic evolution had been operative for an enormously long period before biological evolution started, just as the latter ante-dated by hundreds of millions of years the start of human evolution. Furthermore, just as biological evolution was made possible by the inorganic evolution which preceded it, so human evolution was made possible by the prior development of life. Finally, at the inorganic level only a relatively low degree of organization of the world-stuff exists. But as one proceeds to the biological level, and from there to the psycho-social, the degree of organization steadily increases. The result is the stratified and hierarchical universe which we find ourselves inhabiting (Huxley, 1943, 33-42; 1953, 11-13; 1957, 41-42).

What is the reason for introducing the concept of a 'world-stuff' into this picture of cosmic evolution? The answer appears to be that the concept enables Huxley to say that the features manifested at each of the levels of organization were 'potentialities' of a single substance, successively actualized in the history of the universe. This is a familiar metaphysical doctrine which is designed to make intelligible the appearance of mind at a late stage of the evolutionary process. Mind did not come into being *ex nihilo*. It was 'potentially present' from the beginning. Sometimes, however, Huxley uses language of a Spinozistic cast and talks about matter and mind not as potentialities but as 'aspects' of the one ultimate substance in which they are united. Again, he declares that mind is developed from 'some universal property of the world-stuff'. These various formulations are by no means synonymous. Yet no attempt is made to bring them into harmony.

Huxley stresses the fact that 'the three sectors of the universal process differ radically in their extent, both in space and time, in the methods and mechanisms by which their self-transformations operate, in their rates of change, in the results which they produce, and in the levels of organization which they attain'. What justification, then, is there for calling the process which goes on in each sector 'evolution'? The reply seems to be that in addition to the differences certain broad characteristics common to all the sectors can be specified. That is to say, the over-all process of evolution has the characteristic of being 'a one-way process in time; unitary; continuous; irreversible; self-transforming; and generating variety and novelty during its transformations'. The biological sector certainly manifests these characteristics; but it has no monopoly on them. Hence, to restrict the term 'evolution' to that sector is unwarranted. 'Some term is undoubtedly needed for the comprehensive process in all its aspects, and no other convenient designation exists at present save that of evolution' (Huxley, 1953, 12).

Now the first point to be made about this metaphysical doctrine is that it is in no way implied by evolutionary theory proper. One can accept that theory without being logically committed to the doctrine of cosmic evolution. The history of inorganic nature is not investigated by the biological sciences, and their conclusions do not allow us to infer any of the details of that history. To learn these details we must turn to such physical sciences as astronomy or cosmology. Only then can we say whether or not the history of the physico-chemical aspects of the universe exemplified the broad characteristics which would entitle us to call what happened 'inorganic evolution'. Huxley would doubtless have no quarrel with this contention, whose truth, indeed, seems obvious. But from the standpoint of the question being discussed in the present chapter, the contention enables us to affirm that 'cosmic evolution' is not a metaphysical implication of modern selectionist or any other scientific theory about the history of terrestrial life.

Considered independently, as a possible world-picture, cosmic evolution has many attractions. Yet it gives rise to difficulties which, though not necessarily insurmountable, are nevertheless substantial. One or two of these difficulties may be mentioned in passing.

The proposal to call the first phase of the over-all process, 'in-

L

organic evolution', needs to receive some support from the results of physical cosmology. Otherwise, the proposal will be quite arbitrary. If the prevailing cosmological theory represented the whole physico-chemical universe as developing in time, the proposal would obtain a powerful measure of support. The proposal would be seriously undermined if the prevailing cosmological theory represented the whole physico-chemical universe in non-developmental terms (e.g. as having existed always in a 'steady-state'). Now it happens that both these theories have their advocates in contemporary cosmology (Cf. Bondi, 1952). Indeed, most of the results of this science are subject to controversy, so that certain critics have even refused to admit that it is a 'science' at all. Until a more settled outlook is achieved here, it is impossible to tell whether the proposal to speak of 'inorganic evolution' is justifiable or not. Certainly, in the face of so much disagreement it would be rash to jump to conclusions. And since the idea of inorganic evolution is an essential part of the doctrine of cosmic evolution, the latter also must be considered dubious at present.

Even if this difficulty is overlooked, a serious one remains. It arises from the reasonable demand that a close degree of similarity ought to be established between the first and second phases of the over-all process, if the same term, 'evolution', is applied to both. Huxley has emphasized that they do differ radically in a number of respects. But he has also emphasized that they share a group of characteristics, and it is because of these that he feels entitled to treat the two phases as 'sectors' of a single process. Yet the alleged common characteristics are precisely what create trouble when scrutinized more closely. I will select a couple of examples to illustrate the difficulty.

It may be plausible to describe the history of inorganic and organic phenomena as 'continuous' in a vague sense. To do this, however, is to overlook the fact mentioned in Chapter II, p. 36, that 'continuity' is ascribable to organic evolution only in a metaphorical way, the ground of the metaphor being the reproductive process by which members of one generation give rise to those of the next. This process enables life to be 'continued'. But nothing resembling biological reproduction occurs, as far as we know, in the inorganic world. Hence even if that world undergoes some sort of development in time, the development is not continuous in the way organic evolution is. The common characteristic here is delusive.

A like difficulty crops up if we consider the 'self-transforming' feature attributed to cosmic evolution. Preceding chapters have indicated how the self-transformation effected by pre-human organic evolution depended on such things as the power of genetic units to produce copies of themselves and to undergo periodic mutations, the capacity of most living things to adapt successfully to the environment, the process of differential reproduction, etc. These are uniquely organic phenomena, lacking any known analogues in the inorganic domain. The self-transforming process of human evolution, with its dependence on cultural agencies such as tool-using, languages and conceptual thought, is even farther removed from the possibility of comparison with physico-chemical activities. If the inorganic sector did manifest 'self-transformation', this must have been altogether different from what happened after the history of life commenced. Surely, then, it is illegitimate to suppose that 'self-transformation' in a univocal sense represents a feature common to 'the historical aspect of all phenomena'. This particular foundation for a belief in cosmic evolution is insubstantial.

Certain other questions which bear on the above topic (e.g. in what sense, if any, is biological evolution irreversible?) will be dealt with below. The object of the present section has merely been to focus attention on one specific world-picture and to underline the fact that it cannot be derived from evolutionary theory proper. Perhaps nobody would wish to contend that it can be so derived. Yet advocates of cosmic evolution must surely believe that even if their metaphysical doctrine is not dependent exclusively, or even mainly, on the conclusions of the biological sciences, it must not be incompatible with any of those conclusions. I suspect that most advocates of the doctrine go much farther than this and hold that the conclusions of the biological sciences provide positive support for their world-picture. It therefore seemed worth alluding briefly to *prima facie* difficulties which the world-picture has to remove in order to be given serious consideration. I do not profess to have shown either that cosmic evolution is to be accepted or that it is to be rejected. I have only pointed out that it is not a 'metaphysical implication' of evolutionary theory.

Although this theory may have no discernible consequences for our interpretation of 'the universe at large', it may have consequences for our interpretation of what has taken place on the earth. Henceforth, our discussion will be concerned with the terrestrial scene; and we will take up several broad questions which arise when the conclusions of evolutionary theory about that scene are construed metaphysically. At the centre of most of these questions an important issue will turn out to be that of deciding whether certain basic concepts can or cannot be used in ways which occur neither in ordinary discourse nor in the strictly scientific discourse of biology.

3. HAS EVOLUTION GENERATED NOVELTIES?

It is appropriate in biology to make assertions about evolution as a single historical process. Such assertions are high-level abstractions which obtain their scientific meaning from connections, often very indirect, with what is empirically observable. When these same assertions are interpreted metaphysically, they are taken to be about an individual process which, though not empirically observable, nevertheless has an existential status of its own, quite apart from any scientific theories concerning it. In the present section I want to consider the question whether this process can be said to have generated 'novelties' during its history.

One reason why this question comes up is inherent in the etymology of the word 'evolution'. Its root meaning is 'to unfold' or 'to unroll' what has been folded up. The word applies quite literally in the etymological sense to the series of changes by which, e.g. a rosebud becomes a full-blown rose. Now this root meaning has sometimes been carried over, with certain qualifications, into metaphysical interpretations of phylogenesis. Thus the course of evolution has been regarded as successively bringing to light 'the inherent potentialities of the fundamental substance, protoplasm' (Clark, 1930, 216). Or again, it has been suggested that evolution was 'an unpacking of an original complex which contained within itself the whole range of diversity which living things present' (Bateson, 1914, 640). These 'preformationist' views imply that no genuinely new phenomena have arisen in the history of life. All the organic forms which have come into existence were already present as real potentialities at the start of that history. Evolution simply unfolded or unpacked what was there from the beginning.

Few, if any, would wish to speak in such terms today. Preformationist theories long ago disappeared from embryology. They are equally out of place in thinking about the evolutionary process. Furthermore, it is now considered probable that biological evolution began not with some protoplasmic substance, but with rudimentary genes which had the power of self-copying. Protoplasm arose as the by-product and tool of gene action (Cf. Muller, 1957). But it is completely unbelievable that these rudimentary genes contained the hereditary potentialities for the *whole* of subsequent life. Hence evolution has ceased to be thought of in terms of unfolding, unrolling or unpacking. It is held to be 'epigenetic' rather than 'preformationist'. The occurrence of novelties, in some sense, has to be recognized. But in what sense?

One usable criterion may be set up as follows. All those organic structures or characters which did not result from small-scale modifications of pre-existing structures or characters are to be called 'novelties'. This means that micro-evolutionary changes fail to produce anything novel, *stricto sensu*, even when their cumulative effects over a long period are substantial. An organ which increases its size gradually, even if it becomes twice as large as it originally was, remains the same organ. Sometimes structural alterations brought about through micro-evolution can only be understood in the light of comparative morphology. 'Thus, the larynx of the mammal can be shown to be derived from the gill-slits of the fish and their skeleton; hair in mammals and feathers in birds are probably derived from reptilian scales. There are also other types of evolutionary change that should be regarded as modifications of characters already present in the body' (Carter, 1957, 183). In short, according to this criterion, the vast majority of phenomena which have occurred since the beginning of evolution are not to be accounted 'novelties'.

The phenomena which can be so described are those associated with macro-evolution. They are consequences of the 'large steps' which we are obliged to infer has taken place occasionally in evolution, although we have no direct evidence of them. Some of the earliest of these steps have been plausibly reconstructed by Wright (1949). The first was the formation of individual genes, the simplest entities to be subject to mutation and selection pressures, and therefore the first entities to evolve. The assemblage of many genes to form one organic structure, the cell (or perhaps the chromosome), was the second great forward step. Then came the development of cells capable of conjugation and reduction, from which arose a more complex structure, the interbreeding species. Its constituents at the simplest level were unicellular organisms. Later came multicellular organisms, whose presence enormously increased the scope for selection. They 'may on this account be considered the fourth great step in evolution' (Wright, 1949, 472). After both genes and interbreeding species appeared, they were presumably subject to micro-evolutionary changes extending over long periods. Now genes, chromosomes, cells, interbreeding species and multicellular organisms, certainly qualify for the description of 'novelties' in the evolutionary process. They did not result from small modifications of pre-existing structures, but were genuinely new phenomena. The same is true in the case of other large steps of evolution, such as the ones which gave rise to the mammals or the birds from the reptiles.

Those who recognize evolutionary novelties sometimes employ linguistic formulations to which exception may be taken. One such formulation is the familiar phrase, 'the emergence of novelties'. The difficulty about this phrase is that it does not readily lose its preformationist overtones, because of the word 'emergence'. In its popular meaning, the word suggests a coming to the surface of what was previously existent, although submerged or hidden. Fishes, whales and submarines emerge from beneath the water; rabbits and foxes emerge from their burrows; and so on. The evolutionary novelties of which we have been speaking did not emerge in this sense. A similar objection can be made to the phrase 'emergent evolution'. McGilvary (1956) proposed that a phylogenetic theory which allowed for the periodic occurrence of novelties should be called 'innovative evolution'—a proposal that has much to recommend it. But perhaps 'emergent evolution' has now acquired a sufficiently specialized meaning to insulate it from preformationist interpretations.

Another difficulty has cropped up when novelties are discussed in connection with some highly general theory about their causes. One popular view is that they are caused by pre-existing elements entering into novel combinations. 'Living evolution is producing new combinations of old parts. . . . "New" signifies here no more than a fresh arrangement, a reconstruction, a novel combination, of parts, the parts themselves not other than those existent before. . . . It is in fine after all a reshuffling' (Sherrington, 1953, 128-129). Nowhere has anything been generated de novo.

This manner of speaking is not very satisfactory. It leads us to imagine that evolutionary novelties are like unusual hands in a card game; for instance, thirteen spades at bridge. Then we may think that just as different hands are made up of individual playing cards in different combinations, so the novelties which occur in evolution must be made up of standard units. The mistake here is patent. There is no set of evolutionary 'playing cards' whose reshuffling can account for *all* phylogenetic novelties. In the early stages of life's history, at any rate, new structures (e.g. cells) formed of smaller parts (e.g. genes and protoplasm) must have subsequently become parts for larger new structures (e.g. interbreeding species or multicellular organisms). Presumably few people today would want to defend a simple 'reductionist' view according to which, say, the reshuffling of fundamental particles (electrons, protons, neutrons, etc) is sufficient to account for the total array of organic forms, including all the novelties. To reject such a view, of course, is not to deny that the reshuffling of genetic factors played an important part in determining the products of evolution. But Sherrington's phraseology seems to involve much more than that.

As long as no generally accepted theory about the causes of macro-evolution exists, we are not in a position to account for the factors which have generated phylogenetic novelties. If it should turn out that macro-evolution was simply compounded of microevolutionary events, then the question whether novel phenomena have really occurred might need to be reconsidered. At present we can scarcely avoid the conclusion that novelties have occurred. That is to say, looking at the evolutionary process *in toto*, we seem obliged to suppose that at critical points previously nonexistent wholes or systems were formed. These systems exhibited new characters and became subject to laws which could not be derived from the laws sufficient to explain the behaviour of their constituent parts in relative isolation. Without supposing this, how could any process connect the first rudimentary living things, the protogenes, and the enormously diverse, complex organisms which now inhabit the earth? Furthermore, it is difficult to understand how such novelties could have occurred unless, as mentioned earlier (Chapter III, pp. 89-90), wholly new genetic factors were formed—either new genes or new genetic systems—as evolution proceeded. Many problems in this area are still unsolved; but little doubt attaches to the assertion that evolution has indeed generated novelties.

4. HAS EVOLUTION AN OVERALL DIRECTION?

In raising the question whether the evolutionary process has an
overall direction, it will be well to clear up two possible misunderstandings.

(A) In Chapter III, pp. 109-12, it was pointed out that natural
selection is appropriately spoken of as a 'directive' factor in evolution. The significance of this way of speaking is made clear
within the framework of evolutionary theory by showing how
selection tends to produce orderly changes in populations. An
opposite, randomizing tendency is introduced by the genetic
factors, especially by mutations. Thus at every stage evolution is,
according to modern selectionist theory, the result of the inter-
play of factors which operate in a random manner and factors
which are non-random or directive. This conclusion, however, is
drawn in a scientific context. It does not allow a settlement of the
question we are about to consider.

(B) The concept of 'direction' has a scientific home in paleontology where it is used in the description of trends. These are
sequences of fossils which show steady changes of a character or
group of characters for very long stretches of time (e.g. $10^6 - 10^7$
years). Each fossil sequence represents a trend which is said to
have a direction. When the changes are plotted on a graph, it
may be found that a straight line can be drawn through them;
or it may be found that only a uniform curve can be drawn
through them. In the former case, the trend is said to be 'rectilinear' or 'orthogenetic'. In the latter case, the trend is said to be
non-rectilinear, though continuous and directional. Now the
question to be considered in this section involves the transferring
of the concept of 'direction' (and perhaps also the concept of
'trend') from paleontological discourse to discourse about the total
history of life. The concept is thereby greatly generalized. One
of our concerns will be to see whether such transference and
generalization lead to any illuminating results.

Is there a sense in which the evolutionary process as a whole
can be regarded as a trend? If the answer were to be affirmative,
we could conclude that the process has an overall direction and
could then proceed to inquire what the direction is. To justify an
affirmative answer, while retaining the paleontological meaning

of 'trend', we would have to show that throughout the whole of evolution there has been a steady change of the same kind in some character or characters belonging to all living things. To show this, it may be contended, while admittedly difficult, is not impossible. Appeal might be made, for example, to the large-scale features of evolution mentioned in Chapter II, pp. 38-42. We might argue that the history of life has been marked by a steady increase in the number of organisms and the number of species of organisms on the earth; or by a net increase in the gross size, complexity and all-round efficiency of organisms, etc. Surely we can utilize one or more of the above features to specify a trend which is co-extensive with the totality of evolution?

To this line of argument there is a formidable objection. If the fossil record makes one thing clear, it is that the course of evolution has been neither steady nor straightforward. It has exemplified 'the utmost diversity in every respect, including rate, directness of trend, progress in complexity, and amount and nature of branching of phyletic lines' (Wright, 1952). Discussions of evolution have sometimes assumed that the history of life has been a relatively simple divergence and successive rise of the different phyla, classes, orders, families, etc. But this picture of an orderly, uninterrupted march of the various organic forms to their modern condition is quite wrong. The total history of life is much more accurately described by such adjectives as 'complicated', 'fitful' and 'erratic' (Cf. Simpson, Pittendrigh and Tiffany, 1957).

The force of this objection seems to be irresistible, since it is based on the authority of the fossil record. Yet one might take the stand that all the objection rules out is any attempt to characterize evolution as a rectilinear trend. It cannot be symbolized by a straight line. However, more than this is surely implied. The objection also discredits other models which have had considerable vogue—for instance, that of a 'ladder of life' built up rung by rung from the lowest organisms to the highest; or that of a phylogenetic 'tree', carefully pruned by natural selection so that it has grown in an orderly bifurcation of trunk, branches and twigs. What the objection implies is that evolution viewed in the large not merely fails to be a rectilinear trend, but fails to be a trend of any sort, in the paleontological meaning of 'trend'. To the question whether the phylogenetic process manifests a continuous change of the same sort in any feature of all organisms, the answer must be negative.

Let us next inquire whether there is not some other way of ascertaining the propriety of asserting that evolution has an overall direction. For nothing that has been said so far implies that evolution may not be characterized as having a direction, even though it is not characterizable as a 'trend' in the paleontological sense. One approach which looks promising is to reflect on the contention that evolution has the property of being irreversible. May it not be that the irreversibility of evolution is just the feature needed to enable us to talk about its overall direction?

Before an opinion can be formed about this matter, we must make a distinction. To ask whether evolution *in toto* is irreversible is different from asking whether all or most trends within evolutionary history are one-way processes. The latter is a scientific question, the classical form of which is associated with the name of Dollo, the author of a doctrine subsequently called 'Dollo's Law'. The gist of this law is that when in the course of evolution an organ or character disappears completely, that same organ or character cannot be evolved a second time, though some substitute for it may be developed. The full return to an earlier stage is not only something never observed in any paleontological series, but something which cannot happen. Whether Dollo's contention be called a 'law' or a 'mere rule', is a matter of secondary significance. The primary consideration is that it raises an issue which can be dealt with on scientific grounds. The issue is one internal to the framework of evolutionary theory.

There appears to be agreement that Dollo's Law is broadly sound, provided it is interpreted statistically. Since organs and characters are genetically conditioned, and since any mutation may be reversed, it is not impossible for an organ or character which has disappeared to arise again in environmental circumstances akin to those which prevailed before the loss. Yet the probability of such a recurrence is low. For organs and characters in all the higher forms of life have a complex genetic basis. Hence the reappearance of any one of these organs or characters would require that numerous mutations be reversed contemporaneously, and the chances of this happening are very small. Accordingly, the scientific verdict seems to be that Dollo's Law is acceptable only if it is regarded as a statistical rule which affirms the extreme improbability of the reversal of a trend leading to the loss of some organ or character. Even in cases where man has been able, by selective breeding, to bring about a restoration of an ancestral possession (e.g. the restoration of the hind little toe in the domestic guinea-pig), it can be argued that the genetical basis of the restored item is never *exactly* what it was when the item existed before. Slight genetical differences between the two occurrences are almost certain to be present.

It will be evident that Dollo's Law applies only to trends which lead to the *loss* of some organ or character. But any one of these trends may be the 'reversal' of a trend by which the organ or character was acquired in the first place. Hence trends of the latter sort are by no means irreversible. It may be highly improbable that an organ or character which has disappeared will be revived. From this contention nothing follows with regard to the probability of an item which has been evolved subsequently disappearing. Independent evidence, however, shows that very often in evolutionary history organs and characters will disappear when members of a species alter their way of life. Parasites provide many illustrations of this. Accordingly, the acceptance of Dollo's Law, while it commits us to the view that some evolutionary trends are irreversible, does not require us to hold that all, or even most, trends are so. A *fortiori*, the law does not commit us to the irreversibility of evolution as a whole.

Returning to the metaphysical aspect of the matter, I will take note of an argument whose core is as follows. The history of life on the earth is a vast natural process through which changes in populations of organisms have come about. Now there is a well-established principle of physics, the second law of thermodynamics, or law of entropy, which applies to all real processes in nature, and which implies that such processes are irreversible. More precisely, it implies that the probability of a real process being reversible approximates to zero. Since the evolutionary process is indubitably real, it must come under the governance of this law, and hence be one-directional. Like 'time's arrow' itself, evolution is unavoidably vectorial.

Opposed to this is an argument which contends that the second law of thermodynamics does *not* apply to living things, or at any rate does not apply to their evolution. On the contrary, there is reason to think that organic processes generally violate the law. For it is characteristic of the phenomena to which the law applies that they never involve a decrease of the quantity called *entropy*. This means, *inter alia*, that they never pass from states of smaller to states of greater organization. Thermodynamic changes lead to an increase of entropy, i.e. they lead to an increase of randomness or disorder of the elements in a given system. A paradigmatic instance is the increasing randomness and uniformity of molecular motion which always come about when gases at different temperatures are brought together in a separate container. But two of the most characteristic organic processes, ontogenetic development and phylogenetic evolution, display precisely the opposite tendency. They go towards states of greater organization and heterogeneity from relatively unorganized, uniform starting points. Moreover, they do this in relatively random surroundings. Is it not evident, then, that these organic processes cannot be subject to the second law of thermodynamics? Indeed, organisms can properly be called 'cheats in the game of entropy. They alone seem able to breast the great stream of irreversible processes. These processes tear down; living things build up. While the rest of the world seems to move towards a dead level of uniformity, the living organism is evolving new substances and more and more intricate forms' (Lewis, 1926, 178). It is certain, therefore, that we cannot deduce the irreversibility of evolution from the second law of thermodynamics, no matter how solidly the latter may be established in the organic world.

The issues raised by these two arguments have been treated at length by various authors and need not be reviewed in detail here (Cf. Muller, 1939; Needham, 1943; Blum, 1951, 1955). Certain oversimplifications and misinterpretations may, however, be briefly noted.

Classical thermodynamics is a theory which deals with states of equilibrium in isolated or closed physical systems only, i.e. systems which do not exchange energy with the rest of the universe. The second law of thermodynamics (in one of its formulations) affirms that entropy can never decrease in such systems. Hence whatever changes take place there are irreversible. But in non-isolated or open systems, where exchange of energy with the surroundings does occur, entropy can decrease, and reversible processes are therefore possible. Here the second law in its classical form does not apply. Now organisms and populations of organisms are open systems. They carry on continuous energy exchanges with their environment. Hence we cannot legitimately deduce as a consequence of the second law that their development or evolution must be irreversible. Accordingly, the first argument stated above is invalid.

On the other hand, it by no means follows that living organisms or the process of evolution *violate* the principles of classical thermodynamics. Within an open system there may occur a decrease of entropy and a general movement towards greater heterogeneity and complexity of organization. Yet this is a local phenomenon which is possible only because in the more inclusive energy-system of which the open system is a part, entropy increases in accordance with the second law. Now the history of living things on the earth would not have been the incremental, differentiating, complicating and progressive affair it was had solar energy not been streaming down on the planet from the start of that history. If we ignore the dependence of living things on this energy and think of the history of life as an isolated series of happenings, we will be tempted to conclude that what has occurred is a violation of thermodynamic principles, and to describe organisms as 'cheats in the game of entropy'. But if we wish to assess the situation thermodynamically, we cannot neglect the energy exchanges which go on in our solar system—let alone those which go on in the whole physical cosmos—for upon these energy exchanges both organisms and their evolution depend. And in the solar system alone there has undoubtedly been a vast increase of entropy since life began on the earth (Blum, 1955). Accordingly, what has happened in evolution is entirely compatible with the second law of thermodynamics, even though the latter in its classical form does not apply directly either to ontogenetic or phylogenetic events. What is true of a whole is not necessarily true of each of its parts. On this point the second argument above goes wrong.

There is, however, another way to avoid getting into trouble when discussing this subject, namely to give up talking about entropy in connection with evolution. At least two reasons make such a course advisable. (i) In the context of thermodynamics, 'entropy' refers to a quantity which is the measure of the disorder of the motion of particles in a closed physical system. This quantity is neither observed nor measured directly. It is calculated in terms of other quantities, for example, temperature and pressure. But when people say: 'the evolutionary process involves a decrease of entropy', they are not using 'entropy' in its classical sense. For the evolutionary process arises from changes in populations, not from the motion of particles. Populations evolve or fail to evolve. Particles do neither. To introduce the classical notion of entropy into discussions of phylogenesis is thus more likely than not to encourage confusion. (ii) Thermodynamic order is a state of segregation or separation of physical elements, and thermodynamic disorder is a state of 'mixed-up-ness' of those same elements. A perfect crystal at absolute zero would be an instance of maximum order because one and only one position is provided for each molecule. A gas at 1000 degrees C would be an instance of great disorder, because each constituent molecule occupies successively an enormous number of different positions by virtue of its random motion at high speeds. In the crystal the molecules are segregated. In the gas they are mixed up. But biological order or organization, as Needham has pointed out (1943), is different from thermodynamic order, and is quite compatible with a high degree of 'mixed-up-ness' of physical elements. That is to say, what in the context of thermodynamics is a state of randomness, may in the context of biology be a state of great organization or 'patterned mixed-up-ness'. Conversely, a state of thermodynamic order can have, biologically speaking, no organization at all (e.g. a crystal). Hence the fact that evolution has led to a progressive increase in the biological organization of living things is insufficient warrant for affirming conclusions which utilize the notion of entropy, whose primary application lies in quite a separate domain.

The upshot of this part of the discussion is that the laws of classical thermodynamics cannot be legitimately invoked to establish the irreversibility of the evolutionary process as a whole. The latter neither validates nor invalidates those laws. If this be granted, I think we may conclude that the term 'irreversible', which has acquired a special meaning in the vocabulary of the physicist, does not have the same meaning when applied to evolution (Cf. Lotka, 1945). Let us see whether we can make out what the term means when so applied.

It will be pertinent to consider 'irreversible' along with two other terms which have also been employed to characterize the process of evolution, namely 'irrevocable' and 'unrepeatable'. If we envisage that process as a unique historical sequence of events, extending from the past into the present, then it is irreversible in the sense of being irrevocable. What has happened cannot be altered, and a fortiori cannot be reversed. The same is true of all past occurrences. But this historical irreversibility is quite different from thermodynamic irreversibility. The latter can be predicted to hold of a certain kind of process before it occurs. The former can only be ascribed to a single process after it has occurred. Thermodynamic irreversibility is associated with the capacity for yielding a balance of work, whereas historical irreversibility is just one aspect of the irrevocability of what is past. It is probably wise, therefore, to avoid saying that terrestrial evolution is 'irreversible', and simply describe it as 'irrevocable' (Cf. Simpson, Pittendrigh and Tiffany, 1957).

With regard to the unrepeatability of the evolutionary process, two cases must be distinguished. (a) As a unique historical sequence of events, terrestrial evolution obviously cannot be repeated any more than it can be reversed. For precisely *that* sequence composed of those particular events can never recur. Both the sequence and the events are gone beyond recall. This again is true of every historical series of happenings. (b) Yet it is quite possible to envisage the evolutionary process being repeated elsewhere in the universe. We can easily perform a 'thought experiment' which enables us to conceive that on some other planet like our own, a duplication of the phylogenetic sequence which took place here has occurred or will occur. Such a duplication is neither logically nor physically impossible. Indeed, reasons have lately been advanced by some astronomers and biochemists for regarding it as rather probable. Hence it has to be admitted that the evolutionary process as a whole is repeatable in principle at different spatio-temporal locations.

Now when we think of evolution as repeatable, we are regarding the total sequence of events which constitutes it not as something unique, but as a type or kind of phenomenon. We are also regarding the component events as kinds of occurrences. Yet even when viewed in this way, evolution is not a type of process which can be repeated at a specific spatio-temporal location. Or, to put it more exactly, each instance of the generic phenomenon can occur only once on a particular planet. For evolution is a historical process, and hence some of the conditions which enter into its causal determination are cumulative. Each phase of the process adds fresh conditions to those already at work, so that a return to the precise set of conditions which prevailed at the outset of the process is impossible. 'If there is a sequence of ancestral and descendant organisms, $a \to b \to c$, then b evolved from a and would have been different if a had been different in any respect ... b cannot evolve again from c because c is different from a, and cannot possibly give rise to quite the sort of organisms that arose from *a'* (Simpson, Pittendrigh and Tiffany, 1957, 469; cf. Dobzhansky, 1958). We may conclude, therefore, that a 'repeat performance' of the evolutionary drama is not possible on the earth, although the drama may have been, or may be, performed in other cosmic theatres.

I have argued above that the law of entropy formulated in classical thermodynamics fails to offer a basis on which to specify an overall direction for evolution. But may not a biological law be found to do the job? What is needed, of course, has to be different from any of the general statements mentioned in Chapter III, p. 122. These represented a sample of laws whose instances are recurrent events or patterns of events *within* the evolutionary process. A host of such general statements could be listed, including some which bear the names of their authors (who often exaggerated the importance of what they formulated). 'Cope's law', 'Haeckel's law', 'Williston's law', etc, belong in this category (Cf. Simpson, 1950a). None of these, however, can provide the kind of basis required for ascribing to evolution as a whole a direction, since all are concerned with limited aspects of the total process.

It would appear that what is needed is a law which applies only to the one, unique evolutionary process, or which applies to it as a member of a class of processes. In both cases, the course of terrestrial evolution is construed as a single individual. This amounts to saying that a metaphysical interpretation has been made. Consequently, if a law-like statement could be framed to apply to just this one individual, it would have to be both a metaphysical and an 'individual' law. Yet it is hard to see how anything could combine these two features. Mehlberg has shown that if we are to grant to a statement about one individual the status of a law, the statement must be essentially quantified, i.e. such that (*a*) it is not equivalent to a finite combination of singular statements about the individual, and (*b*) it demands substantiation by established inductive methods (Mehlberg, 1958, 18off.). Whether empirical sciences contain statements which conform to both requirements and which may therefore be called 'individual laws' is a matter open to argument. But a metaphysical statement certainly cannot conform to requirement (*b*). Hence in the scientific sense of 'law' there could not be a statement which merited this designation and at the same time was limited in application to the one historical process of evolution.

Somebody may wish to argue that we can speak of a metaphysical law here in a sense analogous to that of a scientific law, provided we regard the one historical process of evolution as belonging to a class which can have other members. Suppose, for instance, that we could produce reasons for believing that all members of this class are cyclical processes. They are akin to the growth-pattern of an individual organism in proceeding successively through phases of childhood, youth, maturity, to old-age. Each evolutionary process is born, runs its natural course, and then dies out. The statement affirming this cyclical doctrine would be a metaphysical law which applies to the process of terrestrial evolution because the latter belongs to a class of which the law holds. Furthermore, by means of it we could specify evolution's overall direction.

The analogy embedded in this argument presumably consists in the contention that while the supposed metaphysical law is not an essentially quantified statement as all scientific laws are, it is nevertheless like a scientific law in having instances to which it applies. These instances are, however, unobservable. Hence the only reasons which could be offered for believing in the supposed metaphysical law would be *a priori*, not inductive. That such reasons are unlikely to be acceptable may be inferred from the general discredit into which *a priori* metaphysics has fallen. Thus, the various cyclical theories advanced from time immemorial in speculative cosmology have had a conspicuous lack of success. So have theories in cultural history which try to portray the life-cycle of civilizations (Cf. Popper, 1957b). Even attempts in biology to establish a law according to which races or groups of organisms evolve from a juvenile through an adult to a senile stage have been deemed unsuccessful. This is not to imply that cyclical phenomena are absent from the living world. Many such phenomena are known and investigated in ecology (Cf. Allee, *et al*, 1949). But they are all empirically verifiable occurrences within terrestrial evolution, and yield no support for the claim that evolution *in toto* is a cyclical process. I conclude, therefore, that there is small hope of eliciting reasons for accepting the idea of 'a metaphysical law of evolution', and I suspect that even as a vague analogy the idea is logically flimsy.

Up to this point no basis has been found for saying that terrestrial evolution has an overall direction. I now want to suggest a

M

line of thought which may provide such a basis. The line of thought starts from the large-scale features of the evolutionary process which have already been mentioned, but it does not involve any supposition that the process as a whole is a trend. The scientific reconstruction of the history of life, utilizing the available evidence, concludes that in the course of this history there has been a net increase in the total number of environments occupied by organisms on the planet. There has probably also been an increase in the gross size of organisms and in their general biological efficiency. All these are inferences which, if not, conclusively established, are supported by an imposing array of facts and not subject to serious doubt.

This aspect of evolution has been graphically sketched by Simpson as follows.

'If you look at the life of the Cambrian and then at that of today, the first and deepest impression is that of increase. Then there was no life on the lands or in the air; now there is hardly a handful of soil or a rod of the earth's surface or a bit of breeze in which life, large or small, does not exist. Even in the seas the increase is richly evident. No fish swam in the Cambrian oceans, no crabs or lobsters moved along their shores, and even the lowly shellfish were then few, simple, and unvaried in comparison with their present exuberance. Yet if you look with speculative eye at the unknown age when life was just beginning, the Cambrian age of life already represents an increase of life which throws into shade the increase from Cambrian to Recent' (Simpson, 1949, 112).

In view of all this, it seems both appropriate and illuminating to state that one overall direction of evolution is towards the enlargement or amplification of life. The statement is appropriate because it is based on certain well-supported scientific conclusions. It is illuminating because it enables us to envisage the present multiplicity of organic forms in a significant relation with life of the past. The evolutionary process, regarded as a single historical sequence, appears in a light which is not cast if we consider just the conclusions derivable from the theory of evolution proper. The effect is achieved by making the concept of 'direction' serve a purpose different from the one it serves within the framework of the theory. The concept functions scientifically when used to characterize paleontological trends. It functions metaphysically when used to characterize the individual process of terrestrial evolution. And one basis on which the latter characterization can be made is the net increase or enlargement of the quantity, diversity and scope of living things which has resulted from that process.

There is another sense in which it might be be said that evolution has an overall direction. Its basis is the contention that some of the more recent organisms, especially among the placental mammals, are biologically more efficient that any of the earliest organisms. This contention, we have noted above (Chapter II, pp. 39-40), appeals for justification to the fact that only in the later stages of the history of life have complex, highly integrated organisms appeared with such equipment as internal homeostatic mechanisms, a developed forebrain and central nervous system, etc. Because of their improved equipment for living, these organisms have been able to enlarge and diversify the scope of their activities. Unlike the earliest living things, their adaptation tends to be flexible, so that they are viable in a great range of environments. In the case of man the adaptation has included the bringing of many aspects of the environment under control. Accordingly, we have grounds for saying that another direction of evolution has been towards the broad improvement of the biological functioning of certain of its more recent products. To say this is, again, to make a metaphysical not a scientific judgment.

It will be evident from the above that I do not think any warrant can be found for speaking of 'the' overall direction of evolution. At least two senses of 'direction' appropriate to the present context have been distinguished, and there may be others. Furthermore, when we use the expression in either of these senses, we do not have to assume that any trends (in the paleontological sense) exist which are co-extensive with the total course of evolution. We may, however, find it helpful to link the concept of direction with that of a 'tendency', i.e. a type of movement much less uniform and determinate than that of a trend. This would enable us to say that there are tendencies for the evolutionary process to move in the directions specified. But such tendencies would not carry with them any connotation of an inevitable and necessary march of events.

5. DOES EVOLUTION MANIFEST PROGRESS?

Sharp differences of opinion exist among biologists and philosophers concerning the concept of progress. These differences have to do not only with the concept's definition, but also with its status and range of application. Clarification of the issues involved has been made difficult because they often arouse strong feelings of approval or hostility. During the nineteenth century there were ardent believers in progress, such as Darwin and Spencer. In the twentieth century there have been equally ardent disbelievers in progress, such as Inge and Spengler. Certain exponents of the new synthetic theory of evolution, however, have lately been arguing that the concept of progress ought to be revived and applied to important aspects of the history of life. This is the topic I want to explore in the present section.

A cardinal difference of opinion which has arisen is whether the concept belongs or does not belong to the framework of evolutionary theory. Three alternative positions are discernible. (A) Since the concept must occur in judgments of value, and since judgments of value are alien to the sciences, 'progress' has no place whatsoever in the vocabulary of an evolutionist. 'When we speak of progress in evolution we are already leaving the relatively firm ground of scientific objectivity for the shifting morass of human values' (Haldane, 1932, 154). Any attempt to treat this subject falls outside biology and involves philosophy. (B) The concept of progress can be given a scientific definition from which all judgments of value are excluded. It can then quite properly form part of the framework of evolutionary theory and be employed to arrive at verifiable conclusions (Cf. Huxley, 1942, 1953; Thoday, 1953, 1958). (C) The concept of progress cannot be defined without some reference to value. But once this is explicitly done, there is no reason why the occurrence or non-occurrence of progress in life's history should not be dealt with by evolutionists in the course of their scientific reflections (Cf. Simpson, 1949; Herrick, 1956).

It is clear, then, that the present topic has to be treated somewhat differently from the topic of the preceding section. There we were concerned with an expression ('direction') which has an established scientific usage, and our interest lay in discovering whether a metaphysical usage of that expression could be found. Here, as the above alternatives show, we are concerned with an expression whose very status as a scientific term is a matter for dispute. Some evolutionists undertake to define it and put it to work. Others reject it. In view of these circumstances, I will first consider 'progress' as a non-scientific concept whose meaning can be stated in fairly precise terms without departing too far from ordinary usage. This may enable us to discover the extent, if any, to which the concept involves a reference to value. Then I will turn to certain proposals to give the concept biological content and apply it to the history of living things.

Popular thought has often regarded progress and evolution as identical. This is understandable, since in ordinary usage the terms 'progress' and 'evolution' (including their respective verb and adjectival forms) do have an area of common meaning. Both involve a reference to changes going on in the world. Both are concerned with changes of a historical kind. Both apply to a sequence of events in which a systematic alteration of some property or properties occurs. Neither term would be applied to merely random or to periodic motions. A single molecule moving in a gas does not evolve, and a swinging pendulum does not progress. Yet a little reflection on ordinary usage shows that the two terms are far from being synonymous. Consider the sequence of events represented by the vital statistics of a country, and suppose that they show a steady increase in the country's population during a century. It is unlikely that anyone would describe this sequence of events as an instance of evolution. But it might well be described as an instance of progress, provided it was agreed that an improvement or betterment in the country's condition had taken place. Here the term 'progress' implies an act of *evaluation* on the part of those who use it. In short, 'evolution' can be simply a descriptive term; 'progress' is both descriptive and evaluative. Other examples from non-technical discourse could be adduced to support this conclusion.

Even if the above account is correct, somebody may urge, ordinary usage is surely too vague and shifting a basis on which to clarify any concept. The reply to this is that at least a starting-point for clarification is provided. In the present case we can take advantage of the clues offered by ordinary usage to produce a definition of 'progress' which will have a certain measure of precision. Thus we can say that the term applies only to a historical sequence of events which manifests a systematic change in at least one property belonging to the members of the sequence, and which is such that successive stages of the sequence show an improvement or a perfecting of that property. This is only a first approximation to a satisfactory definition. But it brings out the two aspects of the concept of progress, one of them descriptive and the other evaluative. That is to say, a necessary condition of any sequence of events being progressive is that at least one property of members of the sequence must display an orderly direction of change. And another necessary condition of the sequence being progressive is that it manifests an improvement or betterment when appraised in terms of a standard. Taken together, these necessary conditions form a sufficient condition for the application of the term 'progress'.

A refinement of the above definition can be effected by utilizing a distinction which is due to Broad (1925). He distinguishes between 'uniform' and 'perpetual' progress, in the following way.

'To say that s uniformly progresses means that every later state of s is better than every earlier state of s. To say that s perpetually progresses is to assert the following two propositions. (a) If x be any state of s there is a state of s which succeeds x and is better than x itself and all x's predecessors. And (b) if x be any state of s there is no state of s which succeeds x and is worse than x itself and all x's predecessors. This of course leaves it quite open that some of the successors of any state of s are worse than this state or than some of its predecessors. The definition is meant to allow of fluctuations of value, provided that their maxima increase and their minima do not as time goes on' (Broad, 1925, 656).

Thus uniform progress is strictly continuous, whereas perpetual progress permits interruptions, or even temporary reversals, of the direction of change. Neither definition implies that value is inherent only in the successive events which constitute s, or in some terminal event, if such there be. Value may inhere in the whole of s as a historical sequence. Broad even proposes a re-definition of perpetual progress, slightly different from the one just given, to bring out this point (Broad, 1925, 657-58).

Before either uniform or perpetual progress can be ascribed to a historical sequence of events, an evaluation has to be made. Some comments are therefore in order about the standard which the evaluation presupposes. In the first place, it must be an axiological standard, but it need not be a moral one. It must allow the terms 'better' and 'worse' to be applied to the events (or their properties); and although these are valuational terms, they are not exclusively moral in their connotation. 'Better' may mean 'more efficient' and 'worse' may mean 'less efficient' for the achieving of some non-moral end. Consequently, it is surely wrong to say, as some persons have, that all progress must be moral progress (Cf. Ginsberg, 1944). In the second place, the standard of evaluation need not specify a condition of value which the sequence of events can reach. It need only specify a condition of value to which the sequence can indefinitely approximate. Thus in the above definition of perpetual progress, it may easily happen that the value of no state of s exceeds a certain finite magnitude. For although the successive maxima always increase, they may do so at a diminishing rate, and hence s, while perpetually progressing, would approach but never exactly reach a permanent condition of constant finite value. Accordingly, it is wrong to suppose either that progress requires an attainable goal or that progress must be unlimited. Philosophers who have rejected the concept of progress because they believed that it implied one or both of these unacceptable alternatives, are thus mistaken.

With the above distinctions in mind let us turn to some proposals to apply the concept of progress to evolution. The first proposals we must consider are to define the concept in strictly biological terms, so that all elements of value are excluded from it. If this can be done, 'evolutionary progress' will be a scientific notion quite free of axiological entanglements.

At the very start, one possibility may be ruled out. No exponent of the synthetic theory of evolution, as far as I know, would be prepared to advance a definition of progress from which it would follow that the history of life has been *uniformly* progressive. To contend that every later stage of the evolutionary process is better than every earlier stage, so that there has been continuous, universal progress ever since life began on the earth, would be to advocate an utterly implausible doctrine. Hence Huxley, while vigorously defending the idea of evolutionary progress, states that it is 'partial' rather than 'universal and compulsory' (Huxley, 1942, 558). Simpson holds a similar view. 'There is no criterion of progress,' he says, 'by which progress can be considered a *universal* phenomenon of evolution. . . . Whatever criterion you choose to adopt, you are sure to find that by it the history of life provides examples not only of progress but also of retrogression or degeneration. Progress, then, is certainly not a basic property of life common to all its manifestations' (Simpson, 1949, 243). The possibility that evolution manifests *uniform* progress can therefore be dismissed.

Returning to the question of formulating a purely biological definition of 'progress', we may next take account of Huxley's important contributions to the subject (1942; 1953). He aims to provide a biological definition of pre-human evolutionary progress only, since it is conceded that any attempt to define 'progress' at the human level must introduce cultural factors, and hence human values. The proper way to attack the problem of defining pre-human progress is, according to Huxley, inductive. Only by proceeding inductively can we be sure that our definition is based on 'objective considerations', i.e. is scientific and not *a priori* or metaphysical. What he proposes, therefore, is to investigate (i) the characters which mark off the 'higher' organisms from the 'lower' (assuming this distinction to be given); and (ii) the main historical changes by which these characters have been gradually evolved. Biological progress is then to be defined in terms of both (i) and (ii). That is to say, it is to be defined in terms of certain evolutionary results and the paths which have led to the results.

The characters which mark off higher from lower organisms are broadly those noted in the preceding section as providing a basis for affirming that evolution has a direction which consists of a movement towards the increased biological efficiency of some of its products. In other words, the characters are what give higher organisms the ability to adapt to a range of environments, to maintain internal conditions in the face of external fluctuations, and to achieve a large measure of control over their surroundings. The sum-total of phylogenetic sequences, including the sequence of dominant types, through which these characters have been developed is what constitutes biological progress. The sequences disclose a genuine advance, not of the one-sided sort which occurs in specialization, but an 'all-round advance' in viability which leaves the way open for further advances in the same direction. 'Specialization is an improvement in efficiency of adaptation for a particular mode of life: progress is an improvement in efficiency of living in general . . . a raising of the upper level of biological efficiency, this being defined as increased control over and independence of the environment. .... Another way of putting the matter is to say that progress is constantly leading life into regions of new evolutionary opportunity' (Huxley, 1942, 562-64; 1953, 115).

Now it seems to me that this attack on the problem is either a purely terminological move, in which case it is misleading, or else does involve an implicit evaluation which ought to be acknowledged. I will comment on each of these points in turn.

(a) Huxley contends that 'the task before the biologist is not to define progress *a priori*, but to proceed inductively to see whether he can or cannot find evidence of a process which can legitimately be called progressive'. If so, one is entitled to conclude that the biologist must have some *antecedent* conception of progress in mind, for the possibility is admitted that he will *not* find evidence of any phenomenon to which the term 'progressive' legitimately applies. The antecedent conception will be such that he can tell when evidence counts for it or against it. But this does not seem to be the procedure which Huxley actually adopts. Rather, what he does is to describe certain evolutionary phenomena which have been established empirically, and then he *labels* them 'progressive'. Thus, he states: 'There is continuity of improvement between one group and its successor, as for instance between reptiles and mammals. We need a term for the sum of these continuities through the whole of evolutionary time, and I prefer to take over a familiar word like *progress* instead of coining a special piece of esoteric jargon' (Huxley, 1953, 113). This sounds as though the whole problem were merely one of nomenclature. Nothing is added to what we already know about evolutionary continuities by labelling them 'progressive'. We say that evolution manifests progress not because of any empirical discovery, but because we make a decision about terminology.

(b) There is, however, a different way of interpreting what Huxley is doing. We have noted that in ordinary usage the word 'progress' is associated with a procedure of evaluation. In taking over this word, Huxley implicitly retains its evaluative features. For the terms which he employs to define evolutionary progress —'improvement', 'increased efficiency', 'all-round advance', etc —are evaluative. They refer to a movement from 'worse' to 'better'. What Huxley does, it seems to me, is to single out certain characters found among the higher organisms, and in the light of these characters he forms an ideal conception or standard of biological excellence. He then judges that since there are evolutionary sequences in which organisms have conformed more and more closely to the standard as time passed, the sequences in question are progressive. This judgment is an evaluation. More exactly, when he says that progress has occurred between the age of invertebrates and the age of mammals, he is affirming two propositions: (i) there was a historical sequence of dominant types involving the replacement of invertebrates by fishes, fishes by reptiles, reptiles by mammals; and (ii) considered as biological organisms, mammals are better ('more efficient') than reptiles, reptiles than fishes, fishes than invertebrates. Proposition (i) is a reconstruction, proposition (ii) an evaluation. But since we have taken the view that the theory of evolution has just two methodological aspects, a reconstructive and an explanatory, it follows that evaluations do not belong to a scientific treatment of the subject. Hence on this interpretation of Huxley's procedure, he has not succeeded in giving a strictly scientific definition of evolutionary progress.

Another attempt to give a biological content to the idea of evolutionary progress is due to Thoday (1953; 1958). He thinks that the weakness in Huxley's argument is that the progressive is defined as that which *has* generally happened. 'Huxley, in effect, assumes that progress has occurred, and then in masterly fashion shows us what we must on this assumption label as progressive. But it needs to be demonstrated that this basic assumption is sound' (Thoday, 1958, 315). To avoid the necessity of such a demonstration, Thoday undertakes to define biological progress without assuming that it has taken place and without introducing any considerations of an axiological kind. Instead, he appeals to certain general conditions of living, and from these deduces the sort of evolutionary change that must be called progressive.

Starting from the axiom that survival is essential to life, what Thoday proposes is that biological progress be defined as increase in fitness for survival. To appreciate the point of this definition, it has to be understood that the increase is assessed in probabilistic terms, and that the fitness includes both adaptation and adaptability. Fit individuals are those members of a population who are adapted to their present environments and whose descendants will be adapted to future environments. Hence the population is both adapted and adaptable. Biological progress is exhibited, according to the definition, only by those evolutionary changes which raise the probability that the fit individuals will, after a sufficiently long time has elapsed (e.g. 10^6—10^7 years), continue to have descendants. Evolutionary changes, no matter how extensive, which leave the probability unaffected are neutral with regard to progress. And if the changes lower the probability, they are presumably retrogressive.

Now unless I have failed to grasp the purport of this definition, it seems to me to harbour a serious defect. Suppose I wish to find out whether any progressive evolutionary changes have occurred during the last ten million years. I must, according to the definition, consider two probability values: (i) the probability ten million years ago of the ancestors of present-day organisms having these organisms as descendants; and (ii) the probability of present-day organisms having descendants ten million years hence. If (ii) is greater than (i), then evolutionary progress has occurred, since there has been an increase in the probability of survival. Likewise, if I want to determine whether progress occurred during, say, the Jurassic Period, I must ascertain the relevant probability value for that period and for the succeeding period of the same length (e.g. about half the Cretaceous). But can we in practice arrive at even a crude estimate of any of these probability values? Surely Thoday's definition is such that it cannot be given empirical application. If we adopt it we can never tell whether there has been evolutionary progress or not. This is too high a price to pay even for so ingenious a definition.

In view of the above considerations, two alternative policies present themselves. Either we should refuse to employ the term 'progress' at all in discussing evolution, or we should recognize that the term is partly one of evaluation, and requires a reference to some standard which can be explicitly entertained. The second of these policies seems to me preferable because it enables us to say illuminating things about the total course of life on the earth. In the remainder of this section I will indicate what some of these things are. It will turn out that the second policy does not commit us to the conclusion that evolution manifests progress in just one sense, or that progress must be uniform, or that judgments on this subject must belong to the framework of evolutionary theory. On the contrary, we are free to espouse the view that evolutionary progress is perpetual rather than uniform, that there are several different sorts of such progress, depending on the standards of evaluation we adopt, and that the judgments concerned are philosophical or metaphysical, not scientific.

Let us begin by postulating as a standard the proposition that increase in the amount and range of life represents an increase of value. The more individual organisms and the more environmental niches occupied by those organisms, the better (Cf. Miller, 1949). We are then entitled to judge that the evolutionary movement in the direction of enlargement of the quantity, diversity and scope of living things is progressive. Evolution manifests progress because its course has been marked by a sequence of events wherein this enlargement of life has come about. We do not need to demand unqualified constancy or continuity in the sequence since we are utilizing the idea of perpetual progress, which allows temporary interruptions and reversals of the general direction of movement. Here, then, is one standard in the light of which we can say that evolution has been progressive.

It does not follow, of course, that this particular standard of evaluation must be accepted. Dispute about it is quite possible. One might argue, for instance, that the increase of life is bound in the end to produce consequences inimical to life itself. High population density ('over-population') in any environmental niche, or on the earth as a whole, cannot fail to result in intense competition for, and ultimate exhaustion of, the available supply of food. The upshot will be widespread suffering, decimation and even extinction of the populations concerned. Accordingly, the unrestricted enlargement of life is by no means to be equated with increase of value. To this argument the reply might be made that the baneful consequences are due to faulty adaptation, not to the increase of life as such. Moreover, now that man has appeared on the scene, with his capacity for foresight and control, most or all of the baneful consequences can be eliminated. Hence, it can still be maintained that the more life, the better. And so on. I do not want to decide whether the above standard of evaluation is acceptable or not. All I am concerned to show is that only *if* it is postulated can we judge that the expansive tendency of evolution represents progress.

A second sense in which we can speak about evolutionary progress is provided by Huxley's discussion outlined above. Starting from the standard of biological excellence which he implicitly adopts, it is permissible to contend that there has been a progressive movement in evolution toward the production of better organisms. For many of the organisms which have arisen during the later stages of evolution are more versatile, more harmoniously integrated, less vulnerable to environmental changes, etc, than those which preceded them. The ascent of life, though tortuous, has led to an all-round improvement of some of the earth's inhabitants. In this sense it has been progressive. Yet, as we have argued, to make this judgment is to evaluate not merely describe what has happened.

Instead of focusing attention on all-round improvement, we might take as the basis of a definition of progress a special sort of improvement. This is what Herrick does in the following passage.

'Progressive evolution may be defined, for our present purpose, as change in the direction of increase in the range, variety and efficiency of adjustment of the organism to its environment. . . . This involves increase in the complexity of bodily structure, which ensures sensitivity to a greater variety of environing energies and more refined sensory analysis, elaboration of more varied and efficient organs of response and more complicated apparatus of central control. . . . The conclusion is that in the higher animals the life of the individual is enriched. . . . The individual lives a fuller life, that is, he makes a better living as measured by satisfactions achieved' (Herrick, 1956, 125-26).

The implication here is that a state of affairs in which there is a greater awareness of and a more discriminating response to the world is *better* than one in which these functions are less developed. Hence the lines of evolution which have embodied changes leading to this development are judged to be progressive. Again we appraise the situation, for as Herrick correctly remarks, 'an evaluation of some sort is necessarily implicit in the idea of progress' (Herrick, 1956, 124).

A fourth definition of that idea can be given, once we postulate a standard formulated in terms of the notions of conscious control and conceptual knowledge of the environment. We can then specify a sequence of events which is limited to the evolution of the human species. For as we have previously indicated, *Homo sapiens* is the only living creature who has exercised a steadily-increasing control over the world in which he exists, through the use of tools and machines. He is also the only creature who has steadily increased his knowledge of the world, has embodied this knowledge in spoken and written languages, and has transmitted it from one generation to the next. Now if we accept the proposition, 'the more control and the more knowledge of the world man has, the better', we can then conclude that he has certainly progressed in the course of his evolutionary history. Indeed, the tempo of progress has undergone a staggering acceleration within the last few decades. It will be noted that the progressive movement thus defined is restricted to a small segment of the total evolutionary process, amounting to about one eight-thousandth of the period during which life has been on earth.

In Chapter IV, pp. 148-9, we took cognizance of the fact that *Homo sapiens* in the course of creating his own unique environment, the noösphere, has become *Homo moralis*. The capacity to judge and guide his own conduct in the light of moral ideals has gradually increased during the last two hundred thousand years from rudimentary beginnings. How this capacity ('conscience' or 'the moral sense') originated is not something about which we need to speculate here. That it did originate and improve is as nearly certain as anything can be. This is the basis on which we can affirm that there has been moral progress. Collingwood contended that the only sense in which we can describe evolution as progressive springs from the fact that 'it has led through a determinate series of forms to the existence of man, a creature capable of moral goodness' (Collingwood, 1946, 322). Such a view seems unduly restrictive. But at least it stresses the importance of admitting moral progress as a legitimate notion, alongside the other kinds we have mentioned. It should be noted, incidentally, that the admitting of the notion does not imply that the evolution of conscience has proceeded without interruption through the period of recorded human history. For we are not employing the conception of uniform but of perpetual progress. Even if the pessimistic conclusion could be established that man has made absolutely no moral progress in the last five thousand years, it would not invalidate the contention that he has made *some* moral progress in the last two hundred thousand.

Let me now summarize the results of this discussion. First, I think Haldane is right in holding that 'progress' is not a concept which belongs to the strictly scientific theory of evolution. For the concept in its everyday use has an evaluative connotation which even a philosophical re-definition has to retain. But terms of evaluation hardly belong to an evolutionist's professional vocabulary. Second, existing attempts to give 'progress' a purely biological meaning seem to me unsuccessful. Either they turn out to be just the adopting of the word as a label for biological phenomena which would be less misleadingly designated by a technical term having no analogue in ordinary language; or the attempts do not succeed in getting rid of the evaluative features of the concept but simply retain these features in a covert form. Where 'progress' is transformed into a technical term by a definition such as Thoday's, its usefulness may be seriously impaired. Third, it seems most satisfactory to regard 'progress' as partly a descriptive and partly an evaluative notion. It functions in judgments of appraisal which presuppose a standard or standards of value. But in relation to evolution the notion also describes sequences of events of a specific kind. These sequences are established by scientific investigation. Their appraisal is due to a philosophical or metaphysical interpretation. Fourth, when the appropriate philosophical distinctions are drawn, it becomes possible to single out a number of evolutionary phenomena which can be judged to exhibit perpetual, but not uniform, progress. That is to say, in the light of different standards of value, we can point to several historical sequences which are well-qualified to be called 'progressive'. Evolution manifests progress not in just one but in a variety of respects. That statement I take to be another metaphysical implication of evolutionary theory.

Discussions of progress in the nineteenth century often culminated in extravagant conclusions. Progress was said to be determined by a law, or to be universal and inevitable in the very nature of things. The reaction against such conclusions resulted in the complete discrediting of the idea of progress among those interested in sober, responsible inquiry. This reaction undoubtedly went too far. There is ample justification for introducing the idea into discussions of evolution, without retaining any of the wilder connotations given to it by nineteenth century romanticism. Biological evolution is progressive, not because of some cosmic law, not inevitably and universally, but in the limited and definable senses which have been outlined.

6. IS THERE A PURPOSE IN EVOLUTION?

Throughout the foregoing pages the terms 'purpose' and 'teleology' have appeared from time to time in connection with the treatment of particular topics. No special attempt has been made to clarify the terms, however, although their application to biological phenomena plainly raised issues of a controversial sort. I now want to devote some attention to this subject. Since it is a tangled one, which spreads over a wide area, I must impose limits on my discussion. What I propose to do, therefore, is to take the selectionist account of evolution as my frame of reference, and assuming this account to be true, I will try to make out what warrant there may be for employing the concept of purpose (or teleology) in statements about the history of life. Even with this limitation a large number of topics will be opened up. But at least they can be handled without crossing the line into the controversial domain of natural theology. I do not want to become involved in a discussion of 'design' in nature at large.

The concept of purpose almost certainly arose as a result of man's reflection on the circumstances connected with his own voluntary actions. The anticipated outcome of such actions, the goal consciously envisaged by an agent, is his 'purpose' in the most fundamental meaning of the term. Actions are purposive or teleological whenever they are intentionally directed to the attainment of a goal. They exhibit a design or plan, from the observation of which the purpose of the agent can often be inferred. Now this way of speaking is a correct, literal description of what happens in the lives of men countless times each day. It would be superfluous to give examples. The attempt to replace the description by some psychological theory, such as classical behaviourism, which rejects the concept of purpose, is itself an instance of purposive (though misguided) activity. *Homo sapiens*, then, certainly entertains conscious purposes and executes planned behaviour. And since he is an integral part of the evolutionary process, as well as being a product of it, purpose undoubtedly exists, to this extent at least, in biological and cultural evolution.

The temptation has been overwhelming to extend the use of the term 'purpose' by applying it to phenomena quite different from those just mentioned. Without going into the details of a familiar story, we may note two extensions which are important for our discussion.

(A) Machines and their constituent parts are both commonly described as purposive. A watch is said to have the purpose of telling the time, and the purpose of its mainspring is to keep the watch running. No problems are generated by this way of speaking since it is perfectly clear what is meant. The watch is purposive only in the sense that it was designed and assembled by human beings for the attainment of a consciously desired end (recording the passage of time). The mainspring is purposive only in the sense that its function is to keep the watch operating. If it fails to do so, the watch will not serve the end for which it was made. Another way of putting this is that a machine is a mechanical system every part of which is purposive because it has a specific function in promoting the operation of the whole system. Machines exemplify an 'external teleology' derived entirely from the intentional activity of the persons who designed and built them.

(B) The concept of purpose has also been extended so as to apply to biological structures and processes which belong to individual organisms. We have noted above (Chapter III, pp. 97-98) how the concept is implied in judgments that a particular character of an organism is an adaptation. But both ordinary speech and technical treatises employ teleological language when describing what such internal organs as the heart, lungs, kidneys, etc, do. Each of these structures is said to have a purpose—the heart to keep the blood circulating, the lungs to absorb free oxygen and give off carbon dioxide, the kidneys to excrete waste products, and so on. Few of those who use teleological language here think that consciously envisaged ends are being pursued. It is not supposed that either the heart or the organism possessing it first desires to keep the blood in motion and then takes appropriate steps to attain this end. To be sure, speculative suggestions have been made that a primitive form of 'consciousness', and hence of conscious purpose, must belong to cells and tissues. But most biologists who have applied the concept of purpose to living bodies prefer to regard it as designating something 'unconscious'. They are inclined to hold that organisms exhibit an 'internal teleology' with which no conscious prevision need be associated.

This second extension of the term 'purpose' has given rise to a prolonged controversy. Some have contended that the extension generates confusion and obscures crucial issues. Others have condemned the notion of 'unconscious purpose' as a contradiction in terms. Still others have defended the notion, regarding it as

N

heuristically valuable or even essential for the proper description of living things. Woodger (1929) has argued that the description can be formulated equally well by dropping the term 'purpose' altogether and substituting the term 'function', provided we retain the idea that organic functions ensure the persistence of the individual or the population to which it belongs. Agar (1943) proposes to distinguish 'purposeful activity', when a consciously conceived end is involved, from 'purposive activity', where we have to leave undecided the question whether the end is consciously envisaged or not. E. S. Russell (1945) prefers 'directive activity' to 'purposive activity' as the name for the kind of behaviour found only in living things, since this behaviour seldom involves an explicit awareness of the goal towards which it moves. Exponents of 'Cybernetics' (Wiener, 1948; Frank, *et al*, 1948) have urged that what has been traditionally called 'purposive activity' should be scientifically understood in the light of the model provided by self-regulating machines or 'servo-mechanisms'. Bertalanffy (1952) has advocated a non-mechanistic and non-teleological interpretation of vital processes by regarding them as displaying the unique feature of 'equifinality' which arises from the fact that organisms are open systems. These are just a few of the diverse positions taken on this controversial subject.

One conclusion is inescapable. From the standpoint of science we are not entitled to affirm or deny categorically (i) that the internal structures and processes of organisms are purposive, and (ii) that the overt, macroscopic behaviour of organisms, other than human beings, is purposive. What we are entitled to affirm is that these structures, processes and behaviour show an *ostensible* design or plan. The heart, lungs and kidneys act *as if* they were pursuing definite ends. Protective coloration and mimicry *look as though* they were designed to protect their possessors from enemies. Web-spinning and nest-building are *apparently* purposive forms of behaviour. In all such cases the end being sought appears to be that of maintaining individual organisms or perpetuating the populations to which they belong. Accordingly, 'the most superficial knowledge of organisms does make it look as if they were very complex systems designed to preserve themselves in the face of varying and threatening external conditions and to reproduce their kind. And, on the whole, the more fully we investigate a living organism in detail the more fully does what we discover fit in with this hypothesis' (Broad, 1925, 83). The appearance of design is, therefore, certainly manifested by many of evolution's products. That is why biologists are justified in using the concept of purpose when they make judgments about adaptations.

It is easy, however, to overstate the case for apparent design. A large body of evidence exists which creates quite a different impression. The sciences of pathology, parasitology, animal teratology, and morbid anatomy concern themselves with facts which point to a dysteleology, or absence of design, in living nature. Pathogenic parasites, malformations in embryonic development, malfunctioning of endocrine glands, and so on, lead to numerous organic imperfections and monstrosities (Cf. Decugis, 1941). Contemplation of the activities of disease-producing bacteria and viruses, of cancer cells, of acardiac and acranial monsters, of cretins and pituitary dwarfs, does not suggest the presence of purpose, but rather its absence. Yet all these things have arisen in the evolutionary process and must be included in a description of what is found in the organic world. Hence, that world contains phenomena which are hostile to any doctrine of universal teleology. Maladaptations as well as adaptations occur among the products of evolution.

The appearance of both design and lack of design is exactly what one might have expected to find, given the causal conditions specified by selectionist theory. Since mutations arise at random, without reference to the needs of organisms, and since the vast majority of mutations are harmful, they may be manifested as phenotypic imperfections or even as monstrosities. Stable genotypes, on the other hand, will tend to give rise to advantageous characters because of natural selection. Hence, both maladaptations and adaptations can be present in a population. Organisms deficient in fitness will exist side by side with those that are fit. The former will seem 'ill-designed' when compared with the latter. Furthermore, the phenomena we take to be evidence of dysteleology in organic nature often appear so only from a particular standpoint. A population of disease-producing parasites seems profoundly anti-teleological from the standpoint of the organisms they are destroying. Yet the parasites are adapted to live and reproduce in their hosts; and often the developmental cycle of parasites exhibits a 'design' of astonishing intricacy. Biologically speaking, parasitism is a highly successful, though unprogressive, way of life into which certain organisms have been led by their evolution. There is no need to contend that all apparently purposive phenomena in the living world are the result of natural selection, just as it is unnecessary to contend that all phenomena which appear to be anti-purposive are the result of a purely subjective bias on the part of human interpreters. What can justifiably be contended is that both sorts of phenomena are compatible with the main ingredients of selectionist theory.

Thus far the discussion of 'purpose' has been subject to two restrictions. The concept has been treated as descriptive, not explanatory; and it has been considered only in the contexts of everyday discourse and of evolutionary science. I will now widen the discussion so that certain metaphysical issues will come into view.

If we reflect on the total panorama of life's history, the thought may occur to us that there is a sense in which purpose has been operative throughout that history. For is it not the case that organisms normally *strive* to remain alive and to reproduce their kind? Are not self-preservation and the perpetuation of the species *ends* pursued everywhere in living nature? Moreover, these ends have been pursued with the utmost diversity of means, as though it did not matter what means were employed provided the ends were attained. And they *have* been attained with overwhelming success by large groups of organisms, whose 'opportunism' has enabled them to turn very diverse environments to their advantage. 'Every living thing is a sort of imperialist, seeking to transform as much as possible of its environment into itself and its seed' (Bertrand Russell, 1927, 30). This 'imperialism', reflected in the two powerful instincts of hunger and sex, is assuredly purposive. Searching for food or seeking a mate are goal-directed activities. But these activities are presupposed by modern selectionist theory, not explained by it. For according to that theory, 'the statistical consequences of the varying degrees of success of individual organisms in their efforts to live and reproduce give an adequate explanation for all the known major phenomena of evolution when account is taken of the statistical effects of the known processes of heredity in populations of diverse structure' (Wright, 1949, 477).

There may be no serious objection to saying that the two basic 'purposes' of living organisms—to maintain themselves and to perpetuate their kind—underlie the whole panorama of evolution, as long as it is realized that we are speaking metaphorically. For in view of the controversy noted above, we are not entitled to affirm categorically that organisms, other than human beings, do intentionally seek the ends of self-preservation and reproduction. In the case of simpler living things, such an protozoans, it is fairly certain that these ends are not intentionally (i.e. consciously) sought. The same is true of metazoans in general. If biologists were able to study only the behaviour of sedentary animals, it is unlikely that they would use the terms 'striving', 'seeking', 'effort', etc, to characterize what they observed. Sponges and oysters do not exhibit feeding and reproductive habits to which these terms seem applicable. Neither do plants, although the impression we get here may be due to the temporal conditions under which we ordinarily observe them. A very different impression is given when, with the aid of time-lapse photography, plant activities are 'speeded up'. For example, in motion pictures ivy climbing a wall appears to be 'striving' to reach the top and to spread itself out as profusely as possible. The dynamic nature of organic activities is, however, not a matter of dispute. And perhaps no dispute will arise if we assert that in a metaphorical sense the total evolutionary process has taken place because of the two primal purposes which all organisms have: to stay alive and to engender offspring.

This metaphorical use of 'purpose' gives the concept a quasi-explanatory function. But, it may be urged, there are considerations of a deeper sort which entitle us to allow 'purpose' to function in a full-blown metaphysical explanation. Take the large-scale features of the evolutionary process which were regarded as justifying the statement that it has an over-all direction. Must we not try to explain why a net increase of the amount, diversity, complexity and scope of life has occurred in the course of evolution? What accounts for the universal tendency to life to expand, to complicate itself, to diversify its forms, and to exploit every available opportunity provided by the environment? These are reasonable questions. An answer to them which postulates a purposive agency of a metaphysical kind at work in evolution will provide some intellectual satisfaction, even though the existence of the agency may not be scientifically certifiable.

On this approach, the large-scale features of evolution can be regarded as ends pursued by the metaphysical agency. That is why there has been a net increase of the amount, complexity, diversity and scope of living things during their total history. Obviously, then, the agency must be a dynamic power which has some prevision of what it is seeking to attain. If so, we can consider the 'inventiveness' shown by organisms in solving complicated problems of adjustment to be an expression of the power which works through all forms of life. Doubtless the organisms were unconscious instruments, acting without premeditation or intent. Yet their actions were in fact part of a large design which was being progressively realized in living nature. Finally, the postulation of a metaphysical power underlying the whole evolutionary process permits an answer to be given to a question forcefully put by Bergson. 'Un organisme rudimentaire est aussi bien adapté que le nôtre à ses conditions d'existence, puisqu'il réussit à y vivre: pourquoi donc la vie est-elle allée se compliquant et se compliquant de plus en plus dangereusement? . . . Il n'était donc pas impossible à la vie de s'arrêter à une forme définitive. Pourquoi ne s'est-elle pas bornée à le faire, partout ou c'était possible? Pourquoi a-t-elle marché?' (Bergson, 1919, 19-20).

In other words, only primitive organisms existed at the beginning of the evolutionary process, and these organisms were well fitted to survive and reproduce. Why, then, did life not remain in this state? Because, according to the present doctrine, the power behind evolution refused to allow it; or, as Bergson held, because an 'élan' drove life on to take ever greater risks in the movement toward higher and higher efficiency.

If the doctrine just stated were held to compete with scientific explanations of evolution, it would be exposed to the objections levelled against vitalism and finalism which we have already outlined (Chapter III, pp. 80-84). But I have supposed that the doctrine is being advanced as a frankly metaphysical speculation, to 'explain', in some more ultimate sense, certain scientific facts. Even so, however, there are serious objections to be faced.

(i) The doctrine postulates a single power or force at work in evolution. Yet why not postulate several powers? Occasionally, this alternative has in fact been contemplated. Thus, Broom remarks that 'we seem driven to the conclusion that there are various spiritual forces behind evolution' (Broom, 1933, 18). Accordingly, since we are speculating, nothing prevents us from postulating a separate power behind the development of each of the major phyla, for the history of each of them has wholly unique features not shared by the rest. What this objection amounts to is that speculation about metaphysical powers which underlie evolution, since it is subject to no external controls, cannot be other than capricious and arbitrary. It reflects the personal inclinations of the speculator. Hence, any intellectual satisfaction which results from it is spurious.

(ii) If the attempt is made to introduce controls by relating the doctrine to facts other than those it was originally intended to 'explain', then *ad hoc* amendments to it can scarcely be avoided. How, for instance, are we to reconcile the operation of a purposive agency with the complicated, erratic course which evolution has followed, or with the extinction of enormous numbers of genera and species, or with the 'blind alley' of parasitism, or with cases of arrested evolution? What 'end' was served by the amazing episode of the rise and fall of the dinosaurs? And so on. Such phenomena are ostensibly incompatible with the doctrine of a power having foresight of what it is seeking to achieve. To get rid of the incompatibility, the doctrine would have to be amended in various respects; yet these amendments would be quite arbitrary. Perhaps this state of affairs has something to do with the fact that Bergson refused to regard his 'vital force' as having a fixed purpose.

But the most serious objection has yet to be stated. When it is proposed to 'explain' certain large-scale features of evolution by attributing them to the action of a purposive agency, the presumption is that no scientific explanation of those features is possible. For otherwise the postulation of a metaphysical factor would be an unwarrantable intrusion of armchair philosophizing into the domain of science. Yet it is questionable whether that presumption is legitimate. Certainly, we do not fully understand why the great outburst of living things occurred as it did on the earth. Nor do we fully understand why they diversified themselves in the way they did, why some of them became highly complex, why others evolved into self-conscious beings, etc. Part of the explanation is to be formulated in terms of environmental changes, genetic mutations, reproductive isolation, and natural selection. But another part of the explanation may lie in some hitherto undiscovered features of living matter. Lotka (1944; 1945) has suggested, for example, that organisms through their collective activities and effects tend to maximize energy intake from the sun and also maximize the outgo of free energy by dissipative processes in living and decaying dead organisms. 'The net effect is to maximize in this sense the energy influx through the system of organic nature' (Lotka, 1945, 194). Light might conceivably be cast on this tendency by a more complete understanding of the chemical activities of cells, the process by which green leaves manufacture sugar, and so on. We are, therefore, not entitled to presume that the features which tempt us to postulate a purposive agency in evolution will *never* be scientifically explained. The presumption is, if anything, quite the other way.

This brings us within sight of an issue first raised by Henderson (1913; 1917). He pointed out that a study of the physico-chemical properties of the earth leads to the conclusion that collectively they form 'the fittest possible abode' for life. The fitness of organisms is matched by the fitness of the environment. Among the macroscopic properties are the possession of just the right temperature-range (a minute fragment of the total temperature-range found in the cosmos), a dense atmosphere which contains just the right ingredients, an abundance of that most unique compound, water, and so on. Among the microscopic properties are those which belong uniquely to carbon, hydrogen, oxygen and nitrogen, the elements which make up practically all the living parts of organisms. If any one of these items had been significantly different, life and *a fortiori* evolution, as we know them, would not have been possible. The physico-chemical environment, then, appears admirably 'adapted' to sustain the biosphere. Henderson's classical studies have put this conclusion beyond dispute. But can anything more be concluded?

We have every reason to believe that the elements and compounds upon which life depends existed in great quantities on the earth prior to the first living things. Can we not say, therefore, that the stage was 'prepared' for the subsequent evolutionary drama? Henderson suggested that we are 'obliged' to regard the collocation of physico-chemical properties 'as in some intelligible sense a preparation for the process of planetary evolution' (Henderson, 1917, 192). The fitness of the environment is thus teleological, but not the result of design or purpose. Needham contends, rather in the manner of Huxley, that life was implicit in the physico-chemical structure of the universe. 'A cosmic teleology has thus a sound status in philosophy, while at the same time in no way interfering with causal modes of explanation'

(Needham, 1946, 134). For both men, teleology is wholly internal to the system of nature.

A counter-argument can be advanced, however, that we only want to talk about the stage being 'prepared' for evolution because we are viewing the earth's history retrospectively. But suppose we go back in thought to a point of time before life began. At such a point we might say that the physico-chemical properties of the earth are a necessary condition of whatever may come later, but hardly that they are 'preparing for' what is to come. Nothing 'teleological' could be discerned in the situation. Consequently, when we look back from the vantage point of the present, we should realize that life is what it is because it originated and evolved in accordance with that necessary condition. 'If the earth were not fit for living things, they would not be here but, if anywhere, on some other planet in some other solar system (Simpson, Pittendrigh and Tiffany, 1957, 15). The fitness of the environment no more entitles us to infer the presence of teleology than does the fact that the ocean-basins exactly 'fit' the seas which fill them.

To embark on a discussion of this controversy would take us beyond the scope of the present study. I have introduced Henderson's contention not to settle the question of its bearing on a doctrine of cosmic teleology, but as a prelude to a consideration which needs to be kept in view when we envisage the total course of evolution. Since we know that, biochemically speaking, living organisms are almost wholly composed of carbon, hydrogen, oxygen and nitrogen, the combined properties of these elements must influence evolution in two broad respects. (a) The properties must have contributed positively to the forms which organisms have actually possessed in the course of their history; and (b) the properties must set limits to the possible forms which organisms can possess (Pantin, 1951). Hence the array of past and present life is not just the work of environmental changes, genetic factors, and natural selection. This array has also been conditioned by what those four remarkable elements have allowed to happen. In other words, the 'stuff' which enters into the evolutionary process is not completely malleable or plastic, but imposes something of its own character on the results which are attained (Cf. Blum, 1951).

This consideration reminds us how intimately biological evolution is linked with the physico-chemical constitution of our planet, itself a microscopic fragment of the vast spatio-temporal universe. We are also reminded 'to how great a degree it is true that the universe is all of a piece, and that we are all of us natural products, naturally partaking of the characteristics that are found everywhere through nature' (Peirce, 1931-35, V, 613). These reminders form an additional objection to speculations which suppose that a purposive agency began to function when terrestrial evolution commenced. The radical discontinuity implied in such an event is enough to discredit the speculation, even if nothing else did.

It may be urged that unless we posit a guiding force behind evolution, the course taken by the history of life will be blind and pointless. It will be a tale of sound and fury, devoid of all significance. This consequence seems to many people utterly preposterous. Is it not absurd to suppose, they say, that a process could begin with simple, unicellular organisms or 'protogenes', and then, without a teleological agency to direct it, eventually give rise to a Shakespeare, a Newton or a Mozart? Surely the blind play of natural forces cannot account for the difference between the beginning and the end of this process? To be told that the process took place gradually over immense periods of time does not change the situation. What has to be made intelligible is the fact that it took place at all. And how incredible is the view that the process was just a long chapter of accidents!

A reply to this objection from the standpoint of modern selectionist theory can be reconstructed by recalling some matters already discussed.

(a) According to that theory, the course of evolution is not properly described as a chapter of accidents. For at each stage of evolution organisms are subject to natural selection, a factor whose operation leads to non-random or orderly changes in populations. Selection is a directive agency, functioning exclusively in the present with no prevision of the future. Consequently, the adaptations manifested by organisms throughout life's history, so far from being 'accidental' or 'due to chance', are a consequence of the directing factor of selection.

(b) The nature of the alleged 'absurdity' of supposing that a non-teleological process could begin with protogenes and end with genius is by no means clear. If what is meant is that such a process is fantastically improbable the point may at once be conceded. For as we have seen, natural selection is precisely a mechanism which generates an extremely high degree of improbability in its results. The course of evolution from the first living things to the first members of *Homo sapiens* was a highly improbable sequence of events. But there is nothing absurd in supposing that it resulted in part from the functioning of selection. On the other hand, if the 'absurdity' arises from a feeling that the combined activity of environmental changes, genetic mutations, reproductive isolation, and selective processes is insufficient to account for the appearance of genius, it has to be pointed out that according to modern selectionist theory *Homo sapiens* has been subject to cultural as well as to biological evolution. Indeed, cultural factors have increasingly influenced his development since the start of recorded history. They have given him his unique position among living things. No one (I hope) would be silly enough to suppose that this consideration fully explains the appearance of genius among the members of *Homo sapiens*. But the consideration may lessen the force of the feeling that it is absurd to think of the course of pre-human evolution in non-teleological terms.

(c) How appropriate is it to say that unless there has been a purposive agency at work in evolution, the latter is 'blind and pointless'? Are these suitable adjectives to use? Let us try to throw some light on this issue by means of an analogy.

Suppose the postal authorities in a country find that over a given period the number of letters mailed every month without a stamp has increased. This state of affairs is a trend which may be due to one or the other of two sets of factors. (i) Each month a few more of the country's letter-writers may inadvertently mail stampless letters; or (ii) the country's letter-writers may have a well-organized campaign to embarrass the Government, and so each person carries out instructions to mail so many stampless letters each month. In the case (i) it is appropriate to say that the trend which results is 'blind and pointless'. In case (ii) we should say that the trend is 'planned and purposive'. But note that when we use one of these pairs of adjectives, we imply that it makes sense to use the other pair under different circumstances involving the same individuals and the same overt acts. If this implication were not present, it would not make sense to use *either* pair. We describe a man as 'blind' because under different circumstances it would make sense to describe him as 'not blind'. But we do not describe a mountain or a cloud as 'blind', because there are no circumstances under which it would make sense to say that they are 'not blind'.

Applying these considerations to the case of pre-human evolution, it follows that we can properly employ the adjectives 'blind and pointless' in describing it, only if, given the same populations but different circumstances, it would make sense to employ the adjectives 'planned and purposive'. The circumstances required are those in which the individual members of the populations act so as to realize a plan pre-conceived by them. Yet clearly, for the greater part of evolutionary history it was physically impossible, given the types of individuals which existed, for such circumstances to obtain. The devising and executing of plans depend upon the presence of physical and psychological equipment which organisms during this period did not possess. If they had possessed the equipment, they would have been quite different organisms. To say that the course of evolution which resulted from their combined actions in accordance with natural selection was 'blind and pointless' seems as inappropriate as saying that a mountain or a cloud is 'blind'. To put the matter otherwise: just as the exclusion of the word 'virtuous' from the vocabulary of mathematics does not imply the inclusion of its contradictory, 'vicious', so the exclusion of the term 'purpose' from the vocabulary of biology does not require that the term 'purposeless' be included. The series of positive integers is neither virtuous nor vicious. The course of pre-human evolution is neither purposeful nor purposeless.

What, in summary, is the upshot of this discussion? We began by assuming that modern selectionist theory gives a true (though not a complete) account of the causal factors at work in evolution. Then, interpreting the course of evolution metaphysically as a single historical process, we have tried to make out what applicability the term 'purpose' has to it. No convincing reasons were found for concluding that the term can be applied to any metaphysical agency which has guided the whole evolutionary process. The scientific explanation provided by modern selectionist theory, while admittedly partial, cannot be profitably supplemented by a metaphysical 'explanation' which invokes a teleological power operating behind the scenes. Yet to ban the introduction of such a power is not to commit oneself to the statement that the course of evolution has been purposeless.

On the positive side, our discussion has distinguished three acceptable uses of 'purpose' (or its synonyms) in connection with talk about evolutionary phenomena. (i) The great majority of organisms strive to remain alive and also strive to reproduce their kind. These strivings can be regarded as two 'purposes', in a metaphorical sense, which underlie the whole of evolution. (ii) Living things perform many other activities which are ostensibly purposive. Hence the concept of 'apparent purpose' has undeniable heuristic value in biology. It is a convenient expression for describing intra-organic structures and functions; and it is essential for the specifying of adaptations which organisms display. (iii) Only one sort of living thing, namely, Homo sapiens, is known to entertain purposes in a literal sense. At any rate, man certainly does guide his actions in the light of consciously anticipated ends or goals. Hence with his appearance on the planet, purposiveness became an important ingredient of evolution.

This last fact suggests one further remark. Human evolution in the past has undoubtedly been determined to some extent by the purposes which individual men have entertained. Yet the determination exerted has been a sporadic, piecemeal, day-to-day affair. Man has not guided the overall course of his own evolution. And he has obviously not guided his own social and political history. What has happened in both these areas has been very largely 'blind'. What *can* happen in the future has at least the possibility of being 'planned', since man has arrived at the point where his knowledge makes him increasingly able to modify, or even to direct (within certain limits) his own physical and cultural evolution. Should he ever succeed in doing so on a sufficiently grand scale, the evolutionary process will be purposive in a way that it has never been before. A strong case can be made for the view that this task represents the greatest challenge man has faced in the course of his turbulent history.

7. EVOLUTION AND KNOWLEDGE OF EVOLUTION

The final question I want to discuss in this chapter is one which seems to me both important and elusive. It arises from reflection on the following statements, all of which are, in my opinion, true. (i) The theory of evolution is exclusively a production of Homo sapiens, or rather, of a few representatives of that species. (ii) The theory is a well-authenticated body of knowledge about a complex, historical process which occurred on the earth. (iii) This process went on for hundreds of millions of years before a theory about it was formulated, and is presumably still going on. (iv) The most recent product of this process, or at any rate the most recent dominant species, is *Homo sapiens*. Although his unique qualities differentiate him from other living things, he remains like them subject to the influence of evolutionary forces. That is to say, he remains within, or a part of, the process which gave rise to him. Now the question I want to consider is whether these four statements provide any warrant for saying something further—something metaphysical, of course, not scientific—about the process of evolution or about man as a product of it.

There are two lines of thought which might be followed at this point, neither of which I find acceptable. The first is the familiar subjectivist interpretation of knowledge. Applied to the above statements, the interpretation would construe them all as nothing more than conclusions of human thought. The theory of evolution is a vast intellectual construction, the basic material of which is man's sense-data, perceptions and memories. Although the theory purports to describe a historical sequence of events, any statement to the effect that the sequence actually occurred, or that it went on long before any description was given, is itself a conclusion of thought, a mere adjunct to the theory. We cannot 'get outside' our thoughts, sense-data, perceptions and memories to apprehend some 'real' evolutionary process which took place. The most we can admit regarding the phenomena of the remote past about which evolutionary theory talks is that they are potential, not actual. They would have been as now described if they had been investigated by beings with the same kind of sensory, conceptual and linguistic equipment as Western man has developed during the last few centuries. But to suppose that there is an evolutionary process *an sich* is philosophically naïve (Cf. Barfield, 1957).

Closely connected with the above is a second interpretation, forcefully stated by Schrödinger (1954; 1958). He contends that a scientific understanding of nature is achieved by man when he adopts the standpoint of a spectator and excludes himself as a cognizing subject from the world-picture which he draws. By so doing, he confers objectivity on his results. But then, noticing that this own body and the bodies of others form part of the world-picture, man is tempted to conclude that the cognizing subject also belongs to it. The thinker *qua* thinker is within, not separate from, nature. From this conclusion, Schrödinger believes, there flows a 'pandemonium of disastrous logical consequences' (1958, 38). The only way to escape them is to recognize that the conscious mind is alien to the spatio-temporal world depicted by natural science. The sentient, percipient and thinking ego which constructs scientific theories is, as Kant would have said, completely 'transcendental'. What this interpretation means for our particular problem is that the most distinctive feature of *Homo sapiens*, his power of self-conscious reflection, cannot be a natural product which has arisen through evolution.

Neither of the positions just outlined seems to me satisfactory. But it is not feasible to embark on a discussion of their weaknesses here. I have mentioned the positions simply to indicate two lines of thought which I reject. What I propose to do, therefore, is to see how far one can go by taking statements (i)-(iv) above as unqualifiedly true. In other words, I propose to start from the metaphysical view that there is an objective evolutionary process about which we have reliable knowledge, and that man, the cognizing subject, together with his knowledge, in no way 'transcends' that process. Subjectivist and Kantian interpretations of the situation will be excluded.

A first step can be taken by reverting to a matter mentioned in Chapter III, pp. 102-103. Current evolutionary theory, it was noted, does not require us to hold that every character exemplified by a viable organism is adaptive. The vast majority of characters do contribute positively to an organism's fitness to survive. Yet some may well be non-adaptive or even inadaptive. Now *Homo sapiens* is undoubtedly a viable organism, one of whose characters is that he has produced a theory of evolution. Accordingly, we may ask whether this theory possesses adaptive value. Does it contribute at all to man's fitness to survive? Or is it adaptively neutral or perhaps disadvantageous? Let us see whether anything can be made of these questions.

A *prima facie* plausibility belongs to the following argument. If we remember that man's environment is not just bio-physical but also—indeed predominantly—cultural, then it is illuminating to say that the theory of evolution has adaptive value. For a living being is adapted to its environment when it fits harmoniously into its particular niche, and when as a species it maintains or increases its numbers. Putting the matter metaphorically, we might say that a well-adapted organism is to some degree 'at home' in its world. Making itself at home is not just a passive process. Usually, an active transformation of certain aspects of its surroundings takes place. Furthermore, those characters which enable living beings to cope with their environment are adaptively advantageous, whereas whatever inhibits them or puts them out of touch with their environment is disadvantageous. Now the theory of evolution has enabled man to grasp a number of vital truths about the world and about himself. As long as he was ignorant of these truths, or embraced false beliefs about the world and himself, he was faced with the problem of adapting to an environment which was a mixture of illusion and reality. Not knowing what was actually the case about this environment in its totality, man was bound to be hampered in his attempts to deal with it. He could not become truly at home in the world. To the extent, then, that the theory of evolution replaces ignorance and false beliefs by knowledge, it surely has adaptive value.

This contention can be related to a point made in the preceding section. The knowledge man needs in order to modify or direct his future development, must certainly include what he has learned from the theory of evolution. For the theory has acquainted him with major causal determinants of the phylogenetic process. It has also acquainted him with the fact that he is wholly within the system of organic nature, and is dependent in numerous respects for his survival on other living things. He has even begun to get an inkling of the factors which have determined his own cultural evolution. Undoubtedly he has a great deal still to learn. But the really crucial question is whether he can utilize the knowledge he has so as to preserve or improve his adaptation to the environment, especially to the swiftly changing cultural environment in which he chiefly lives. Opinions differ as to the likelihood of his succeeding in this enterprise. It is quite certain, however, that unless he assumes responsibility for preventing the deterioration of his adaptive capacities, man will be overtaken by the fate which befell all the other 'failures' whose bones are strewn along the evolutionary path. Knowledge of evolution must be of crucial significance to him in exercising this responsibility (Cf. Haldane, 1927).

Before leaving the present subject, there is one suggestion I would like to make for what it may be worth. Is it utterly fanciful to regard the theory of evolution as a means whereby certain members of *Homo sapiens* achieve an 'intellectual adaptation' to the universe? For a strong desire does exist among a few members of the species to possess an accurate 'map', drawn in accordance with the best available evidence, which will show them where they belong in the total scheme of things. The theory of evolution provides such a map. It gives them an orientation not so much to their immediate bio-physical environment as to the dimension of their cultural environment which is made up of fundamental ideas or beliefs about man and his place in nature. The desire to be intellectually adapted to the world seems to me to underlie a great deal of the activity that goes on in science and philosophy. 'A philosophical problem has the form: "I don't know my way about" ' (Wittgenstein, 1953, 49e). Not knowing one's way about is a kind of absence of adaptation. Perhaps this is only a figurative way of speaking. Yet I do not think that it is therefore misleading. On the contrary, to speak in this way throws an interesting side-light on the fact that man, as a product of evolution, is the sole living thing to arrive at knowledge of the process which produced him. In relation to his unique nature as a cognizing subject, this knowledge can have adaptive value.

Let us look for a moment at the situation from the standpoint of the evolutionary process. We have accepted the proposition that the process went on for hundreds of millions of years before any knowledge of it arose, indeed, before any knowledge of it was possible. Only when beings with the ability to reason and observe scientifically had evolved did the process cease to be unknown. Only then, one might say, did it cease to be wholly unconscious. This has happened at its temporally forward end, a mere 'split second' ago when the time-scale of life's history is represented by the period of a terrestrial day. It is *as if* the process had just begun, through the medium of the human mind, to emerge from unconsciousness to a dawning consciousness of itself. Furthermore, the situation is *as if* the most intense evolutionary activity were now focused not at the bio-physical level but at the cultural level, especially at the point where knowledge, not merely of evolution but of the universe in general, is expanding at an ever-increasing rate. It is *as if* human culture were the very 'growing tip' of the evolutionary process (Cf. Schrödinger, 1958).

How seriously are these 'as ifs' to be taken? Can any reasons be found for dropping them, so that the statements concerned would become categorical affirmations? It is easy to regard such questions as not worth wasting time on, or even to say that the 'as

o

if' statements themselves are pure fantasy. Yet I suspect that this 'hard-boiled' attitude may be a way of dodging some genuine problems. Chief among these is the problem of determining what significance should be attached to the appearance of conscious-ness and self-consciousness in the evolutionary process. To deal adequately with that problem, a full-scale discussion would have to be undertaken. It is certainly not capable of being solved in a few paragraphs. The problem does not arise, of course, for a per-son who rejects any of the four statements given at the beginning of this section. Nor does it arise for a person who rejects all meta-physical talk about the actual process of evolution. But I doubt whether a definitive argument for either of these rejections can be offered. Certainly, none has been offered so far.

To conclude the chapter, I want to mention a pair of implica-tions of our knowledge of evolution which can scarcely be under-lined too heavily. (A) *Homo sapiens*, as we noted in Chapter 4, p. 149, is not a fully evolved being. He is still zoologically and psychically immature. This conclusion is suggested with great force by the evidence. Yet it has proved difficult to incorporate into our thinking. We have been so deeply influenced by the tradition in Western culture which portrays man as a completed being with an unchangeable 'human nature', that we do not readily grasp the fact that he is still in his racial adolescence and still in the process of making himself. We fail to see that what he is not yet may be more important than what he is. (B) A corol-lary of this conclusion is that man's present knowledge is un-doubtedly inchoate. Despite his impressive achievements, he has hardly made more than a start in the cognitive enterprise. Be-cause of the immaturity of our species, 'for a long time to come we can only hope for naïve and clumsy answers to the major ques-tions preoccupying us' (Rostand, 1956, 6). If human evolution continues for another 20,000 years, the frontiers of knowledge will almost certainly be far beyond those of the present day, per-haps even as far as our knowledge is beyond that of our ancestors 20,000 years ago.

This being so, two contentions appear equally absurd. The first is that man can establish now, once for all, the limits of pos-sible knowledge. The second is that one individual can now achieve a comprehensive understanding of the cosmos, and can embody his knowledge in a final, all-inclusive system. The theory of evolution gives excellent grounds for rejecting both of these contentions. Furthermore, despite its own incompleteness, the theory enables us to see why the significance of many evolutionary phenomena eludes us. *Homo sapiens* has not yet reached the level of intellectual capacity that would permit him to grapple effectively with these phenomena. He does not even know how to ask the right questions about them. Hence he still sees through a glass darkly. Yet the theory of evolution has enabled him to put away many childish things and to replace many false notions by partial truths. Whether he has a long enough future to advance beyond his present intellectual state, is a matter I will discuss in the next and concluding chapter.

CHAPTER VI

IS EVOLUTION FINISHED?

In the first flush of enthusiasm produced by the work of Darwin, his achievement was often compared with that of Newton. Just as *Principia Mathematica* formulated laws which govern the domain of inanimate matter, so, it was said, *The Origin of Species* formulated laws which govern the domain of life, particularly in its historical aspect. Moreover, just as physical bodies must obey the universal law of gravitation, so living things must obey the law of evolution by natural selection. From this conclusion it was an easy step to the belief that the evolutionary process is not just something which happened in the past. The process is continuing to go on without any abatement, and will continue through a future of great length. To most Darwinians in the nineteenth century, evolution was literally a work in progress.

Today this optimistic belief is far from being unchallenged. No informed person can doubt that an evolutionary process has occurred on the earth in the past thousand million years. But some informed persons doubt whether it is now occurring; or, if so, whether it is likely to continue much beyond the present. There are reasons for believing, they affirm, that evolution is virtually, if not actually, finished. In this final chapter I will take up certain of their arguments on the subject and offer an estimate of their cogency. The subject not only has a great deal of intrinsic interest, but it provides an occasion for drawing together a number of the considerations from previous chapters.

1. IS EVOLUTION IN GENERAL FINISHED?

We may begin with a group of arguments based on the large-scale features of the history of life.

(A) Evolutionists are agreed that the basic forms of animal organization, the phyla, have all been in existence for a very long time. No new phylum has appeared for more than five hundred million years. During this period evolution has produced a vast number of variations on a few fundamental themes. But its innovations have been secondary, not primary. Furthermore, by no stretch of scientific imagination can we discern in any type of organism living at present the potentialities which might enable it to give rise to a new phylum in the future. Every type of organism is so fixed in its basic structure, that it is biologically impossible for changes of the magnitude required to begin, let alone be completed. The conclusion here is evident. Phyletic evolution not only is finished but was finished long ago. We cannot reasonably expect that the future course of life will require the addition of any fresh categories at the top of the taxonomic scheme.

(B) What about the categories at the bottom of the scheme? Is evolution likely to produce any new species in the foreseeable future? Let us recall that everything we know about the causes which are operative obliges us to conclude that the phenomenon of specialization always tends to increase. For the chief of these causes, natural selection, either brings about the eventual extinction of a species or else makes it more and more minutely adapted to a specific way of life. In the latter case, the potentialities of the species for further change tend to decrease. As time goes on it is less and less likely to give rise to a new species. 'Evolution is thus seen as a series of blind alleys. Some are extremely short—those leading to new genera and species that either remain stable or become extinct. Others are longer—the lines of adaptive radiation within a group such as a class or sub-class which run for tens of millions of years before coming up against their terminal blank wall. Others are still longer. . . . But all in the long run have terminated blindly' (Huxley, 1942, 571). The situation today is that every species, with the possible exception of man, has advanced so far into its own *cul-de-sac* as to bring evolution at this level also to a stop.

(C) Each type of living thing has an environmental niche or adaptive zone proper to it. Only in this zone is it able to survive and reproduce. Now when one considers the overall economy of nature, one is driven to the conclusion that all the major adaptive zones are filled. There is no vacancy into which a new form of life could move even if it did evolve. The filling of the various zones is said to have been compared by T. H. Huxley with the process of filling a barrel first with apples, then with pebbles which occupy spaces between the apples, then with sand which packs down between the pebbles, then with water whose drops pervade the spaces between grains of sand. Eventually a point is reached where the barrel can hold nothing more. This represents the present state of affairs on earth. All the environmental niches which can support life as we know it are 'packed to capacity'. Accordingly, the evolutionary process must have stopped, and will remain in abeyance until such time as the extinction of some existing form of life leaves room for new forms to arise. Even then the process will not recommence unless the new forms prove to be viable in the vacated zone.

(D) Living nature has been for a long time in an exceedingly stable condition. This fact suggests that the 'evolutionary potential' of life has steadily diminished. Indeed, nature manifests many signs of the onset of old age (Cf. Decugis, 1941). Among these signs are the numerous stationary species or 'living fossils', which have remained in a state of evolutionary stagnation for hundreds of millions of years. Then there are the cases of degenerate forms of life, such as the various types of harmful parasites and disease-producing bacteria, whose virulence seems to have increased during recent millenia. The higher organisms are becoming more and more susceptible to pathological disturbances of cellular and glandular functions, and to the perversion or enfeeblement of normal instinctive activities. Even the plant world reveals traces of senescence. All this points to the conclusion that evolution is coming to an end. Hence man has entered the evolutionary drama toward the close of the last scene. 'Pour conclure, il faut reconnaître que l'Homme est venue bien tard dans un monde déjà vieux, encombré de formes séniles, stagnantes, ou dépérissant lentement. Le vieillissement des espèces vivantes est beaucoup plus avancé qu'on ne le croit communément. Aucune ne peut y'échapper' (Decugis, 1941, 364). Evolution, if not finished, is certainly finishing.

The cumulative effect of these arguments is impressive at first glance. Yet they need to be scrutinized rather closely. For the subject with which they deal is so complex that important aspects of it can easily be overlooked or underestimated. We must therefore review some of these aspects and try to determine how far they affect the cogency of the arguments.

It will be recalled that evolution is in the main a gradual process which involves the slow transformation of populations during long stretches of time. Successive generations of the population undergo small changes in their hereditary equipment and in the phenotypic characters controlled by this equipment. As a result the population can maintain itself in an environment which is altering. More than half a million years are required for such changes to bring about the production of a new species. Throughout this period each generation must have a minimal degree of adaptation to the environment, and at the same time the population as a whole must be sufficiently adaptable to meet future environmental alterations. Adaptability, however, depends on potentialities hidden in the hereditary mechanism. For only when these potentialities are actualized as genetic mutations or recombinations, can organisms develop the characters which will enable them to deal with the changed environment. Sudden, large shifts in the process are at best very infrequent.

Now if we take a short-range view of populations we are likely to be unduly impressed by the adaptation of their members to specific environmental niches. In each instance, the adaptation may be so precise that it is difficult or perhaps impossible to envisage any changes arising in the adaptive pattern. Hence a short-range survey of existing populations tempts us to conclude that they have reached the limits of their evolution. Yet this conclusion ignores the possibility that the gene-pool of a population may contain potentialities for further, and even quite rapid, changes. A striking example is provided by the increase of dark forms of various species of moth in the industrialized areas of Europe. These forms are rare variants under non-industrialized conditions. But when smoke and soot from chimneys alter the environment, the dark forms, being less visible to predators than lighter forms, gain a selective advantage and hence spread rapidly (Cf. Ford, 1949; Huxley, 1942). This phenomenon of 'industrial melanism' testifies both to the presence of adaptive potentialities in species and also to the efficacy of natural selection, for which, indeed, it constitutes direct evidence (Carter, 1951). In short, from a strictly genetic point of view complete loss of adaptability can be safely inferred only when a species has become extinct. That is not to say of every type of organism now alive that it has potentialities for further evolution. It is simply to say that we are not warranted in concluding that all or most contemporary species lack such potentialities, and are therefore in a state of stagnation.

This question can be approached from another angle. We have called attention before to the extraordinary inventiveness displayed by evolution in the course of its history. As Simpson has remarked, it 'seems to have tried out almost every conceivable possibility and never to have followed a simple and uniform pattern' (Simpson, 1949, 40). Often multiple solutions of a particular adaptive problem have been exhibited, as if the principle at work were: 'It can be done this way, but it can also be done the other way' (Bertalanffy, 1952, 87). Five hundred million years ago the subsequent course of evolution would have been humanly unpredictable. By a simple extrapolation we can conclude that if life continues on the earth for another five hundred million years equally unpredictable developments are likely to occur. 'To think otherwise is to imagine that with the coming of man, so insignificant in time, the advance and inventiveness of evolution, steadily carried on through an unimaginable vista of years in which no trace of slackening can be observed, has all but come to an end' (Ritchie, 1940, 267). Only human conceit, not an impartial survey of the evidence, could motivate such a conclusion.

These general considerations, some may say, do little to diminish the force of the contention that in a world where organisms are highly specialized and adaptive zones fully occupied, evolution must have stopped. To this the reply can be made that it is questionable whether all or most of the million and a half species now on earth *are* 'highly specialized' in any precise sense. All of them are certainly specialized in the sense that each species is adapted to its particular environmental conditions. But, as we have seen, adaptation is a process subject to different degrees, and not in the least incompatible with the gradual production of new species. Increasing specialization does restrict the evolutionary possibilities of a group. Yet it does not eliminate them entirely. As for the alleged 'packing' of adaptive zones with life, expert opinion is by no means agreed that this has actually happened. Certainly fewer zones with large-scale possibilities for expansion on the part of organisms are available now than in the past. This fact mainly accounts for the slowing down of the diversification of living things and the appearance of stability in organic nature. Nevertheless, existing zones might well accommodate additional forms of life. Thus it has been judged quite possible biologically for a true aerial plankton to evolve (Simpson, 1953). Huxley's barrel is not demonstrably full; and, anyhow, it is expansible.

If this contention is sound, it engenders scepticism about the view that future evolution can occur only in man. Two different cases should perhaps be distinguished. (i) Suppose *Homo sapiens* were to disappear completely from the earth without affecting other species. Then it is unlikely that any of the latter, even species most closely related to him, would be able to evolve to the point where they had manual and mental abilities similar to man's. 'In the ten or twenty million years since his ancestral stock branched off from the rest of the anthropoids, these relatives of his have been forced into their own lines of specialization, and have quite left behind them that more generalized stage from which a conscious thinking creature could develop. . . .If man were wiped out, it is in the highest degree improbable that the step to conceptual thought would be taken again, even by his nearest kin' (Huxley, 1942, 571). Hence future cultural evolution depends wholly on mankind. (ii) But the disappearance of *Homo sapiens* would probably not terminate all evolution. It would be exceedingly rash to assert that *not one* of the million or more species now extant has any evolutionary possibilities. 'Nobody can foresee which group might evolve in such a way that it would become predestined to take over man's supremacy in the world as well as, though not necessarily, to outstrip *Homo sapiens* effectively in the capacity and quality of his brains' (Umbgrove, 1950, 195). Even if all vertebrates became extinct, can we say that evolution would not continue among the remaining animals and plants? Such a statement is most implausible in the light of all that we know about life's history.

The argument of Decugis that the living world now exhibits signs of senility has to face the objection, mentioned in Chapter II, pp. 31-32, to a like argument used of populations and races. Ageing is an ontogenetic, not a phylogenetic, process. Individuals grow old and senile. There is nothing which entitles us to apply those adjectives, even metaphorically, to populations or to evolution in general. It is difficult to be sure what is meant by saying that the evolutionary potential of life has diminished. Possibly some analogy is intended between the system of living nature and a closed physical system in which the potential energy is approaching zero. Yet the appropriateness of such an analogy is far from obvious. If there has been a slackening of evolutionary activity at the bio-physical level, may it not be compensated by the heightening of activity at the cultural level? In that case no overall 'fading' has occurred.

The discussion so far seems to permit the following conclusion. On the assumption that terrestrial life will endure for some hundreds or even thousands of millions of years, then the evolutionary process is almost sure to continue throughout that period. Hence, novel and unpredictable forms of life may be expected to arise, as significant environmental changes take place. But are we justified in making the assumption that life has such a future before it?

Until quite recently the answer to this question was fairly unanimous. It was agreed that barring some cosmic catastrophe, such as the explosion of our sun or the outburst of intense volcanic or mountain-making activity on the earth—events whose immediate occurrence is most improbable—the planet will continue for a long stretch of time to be a suitable abode for life. Physical forces *per se* do not offer any imminent threat to the evolutionary process. Today this answer requires grave qualification. For it has come to pass that evolution's youngest child has suddenly gained control over the most powerful of these forces and may well use it for universally destructive ends.

The situation here is so familiar as to require little elaboration. Man's irresponsible use of nuclear energy may put an end to all terrestrial life and even to the earth itself. Nuclear warfare on a global scale may result in the biosphere receiving a degree of radioactive contamination to which no living thing can adapt itself. Radioactivity may irreparably damage the genetic material of existing species, so that none of the offspring produced will be viable. Indeed, as Sir C. G. Darwin recently pointed out, if man ever detonates a true hydrogen bomb, rather than ones containing (as at present) the hydrogen isotope, deuterium, 'it is extremely probable that such an act would set fire to the whole sea. There would appear a blaze of the brilliance of the sun for something like three weeks or three months, and then it would be over' (C. G. Darwin, 1956, 1115). The occurrence of any of these eventualities would ring the curtain down on terrestrial evolution.

2. WILL MAN FINISH EVOLUTION?

Quite often in the past the failure of a species to adapt to the environment has led both to its own extinction and to the extinction of some other species dependent for survival on it. But never before has one species been a threat to *all* forms of life, as man is at present. Evolution has produced a being who has acquired the power to obliterate both himself and the process which gave rise to him. We will next examine arguments designed to show that this power will probably be put to use in the very near future.

When compared with other living things, *Homo sapiens*, it is said, displays a marked biological instability. One reason for this is that his evolution has been accelerating so rapidly during recent millennia that he is now a badly adapted creature. Although pre-human evolution did not all take place at the same rate, yet its maximum was immensely slower than the pace set by mankind since the end of the last Ice Age. A gradual evolutionary process tends to ensure good adaptation on the part of the organisms which survive. But when the process becomes abnormally rapid, the character of the adaptation deteriorates. This deterioration is apparent in modern man. He has moved so fast from a Neolithic to a civilized mode of life that he has been unable to achieve a harmonious adjustment to his world.

Man's rapid evolution has not given him time to divest himself of a number of primitive emotions and impulses. These probably played an important part in helping him to survive during the early phases of his history. But they now constitute a serious liability. For emotions such as fear, anger and hatred, being physiologically conditioned, can easily reach a state of uncontrollable violence. Under the domination of these emotions, *Homo sapiens* has outstripped all other animals in the performance of acts of savage cruelty and senseless destruction. Impulses such as greed, love of power, and tribal egotism constantly jeopardize humanity's collective existence. They can even overrule the requirements of enlightened self-interest.

Another source of man's biological instability is his fund of surplus energy. This is far in excess of what he needs to establish a settled pattern of life. His surplus energy always tends to disrupt —and has in fact disrupted—every form of social adjustment which he has set up, as the history of civilization testifies. Man's restlessness may be connected with the fact that he belongs to a family of animals which has gone in for the intensive development of one organ, the brain. In the initial stages of his evolution, the brain undoubtedly survived the process of selection because it

conferred great adaptive advantages on its possessors. But now its
activity can easily prove to be that of a double-edged sword. For
the possession of a well-developed brain has given man a readiness
to try experiments which is far greater than that of any other
animal (Cf. Darwin, 1953). These experiments may or may not
be advantageous. The great trouble is that *if* they are disadvantageous, they can be conducted *before* natural selection is able
to test them. Harmful practices cannot, therefore, be nipped in
the bud. Hence it is biologically dangerous for a species to be too
vital and experimental. Little wonder that *Homo sapiens*, with
his hyper-active brain, his primitive emotions and his super-
abundant *élan*, is evolution's problem child !

The upshot of these arguments has been well stated in the
following passage :

As a species, *Homo sapiens* is too young for the adaptive value of
his distinguishing characteristics to be regarded as established.
He may have survived no longer than other types of *Homo* which
have disappeared, and he may still follow them. The entire history
of man may be the expression of a set of unfavourable mutations,
which on the short run appeared favourable as they enabled man
to achieve mastery over all other species, but have still to demon-
strate their lethal character (Whyte, 1954, 127).

It would seem, then, that so immature and labile a being as man
cannot be counted on to use his newly acquired power over
atomic forces wisely. The odds immensely favour his employing
the forces destructively on a global scale. Since this is likely to
occur in the near rather than the remote future, the prospects
for the continuance of evolution even to the end of the twentieth
century are poor. Thus the evolutionary process is virtually, if not
actually, finished.

How cogent is the reasoning just outlined? So many imponder-
ables exist in this area that dogmatic affirmations or denials are
not to be taken seriously. Nevertheless, some tentative assess-
ments can be offered. It may turn out that the general picture is
less black than the above reasoning suggests.

One consideration is, I think, quite indisputable. Man's waywardness, his liability to outbursts of primitive emotion, his
aggressiveness, and his unstable social organization do constantly
threaten his individual and collective security. Allied with these

disruptive factors are highly organized systems of false beliefs and superstitions which prevent the adoption of rational methods for handling major social and political problems. On top of all this has recently been added the possession of unparalleled destructive powers. Even the most stupid must be aware of the resulting shadow beneath which life now goes on.

Is *Homo sapiens*, then, a badly adapted creature, already headed for extinction and likely to take the rest of the living world with him? We have emphasized the point that man is, biologically speaking, an immature species. He has not been on the earth long enough to achieve full stature or to establish a pattern of life adequate to his potentialities. But if we recall that the environment to which he adapts himself is primarily cultural, the quality of his adaptation appears in another light. For the cultural environment is a product of man's own activity. In creating it and adjusting to it, he has changed the face of the earth and drastically altered himself. New forms of inventiveness, heredity and speciation are now at work in his evolution. They play a far larger rôle in determining it than do genetic mutations and natural selection. If we judge human evolution exclusively in terms of genetic and selective factors, we will likely conclude that its tempo has been abnormally rapid. But, in fact, the tempo seems to have been wholly appropriate to a situation in which cultural factors, rather than bio-physical factors, predominate. The evolutionary pace of *Homo sapiens* since the last Ice Age, because it is proper to him, can hardly have generated maladaptation.

Man's abundant energy and readiness to experiment may not be total liabilities. Rather, they have tended to complement his ability to use tools, verbal language and conceptual thought. Much of his energy has been channelled into the performing of constructive activity. Hence, man is not accurately described as a badly adapted creature. After all, the human species has been able to encompass the earth, to increase its numbers at a staggering rate, and to register incredible achievements in technology, in the sciences, and in the creative arts. Surely this is reason enough for thinking that man has found his niche in the universe?

True, he remains an imperfectly adapted creature. For he is still producing his cultural environment, and still striving to increase his understanding and control of it. He is thus continuing the process of his own evolution. The waywardness and instability of *Homo sapiens* are not necessarily signs of mal-adaptation. They may be signs that he has not yet finished his development, and that he is still evolving towards a fully human stature.

Those who believe that he has little chance of succeeding in this arduous adventure may underestimate two facts. (i) Repeatedly, if sporadically, during his career *Homo sapiens* has shown that he can learn quickly from experience and can utilize new knowledge to promote his collective welfare. His capacity to do these things is a matter of record, illustrated most vividly, perhaps, by the history of medicine. Why should this capacity desert him now that he has command of atomic forces? (ii) Every species which has become extinct in the past was the helpless victim of circumstances. It neither knew that it was threatened nor could do anything to alter the course of events. Man's situation is quite different. He not only knows that he is in danger, but he is able to do something about it. What will happen depends entirely on his own behaviour, for which he alone is responsible. There is no inevitable doom overtaking him. Is it so certain that he will fail to exercise his sense of responsibility in the present crisis?

None of the arguments considered here show that terrestrial or human evolution are finished. On the contrary, reasons have been suggested for holding the view that both processes will likely continue into the distant future. Clearly this view is no more than a conjecture. There is no guarantee that man will refrain from exterminating himself, destroying all life, or turning the planet into a star by means of a super-bomb. Nor is there any guarantee that if he eliminates the perils of the atomic age, he will be able to eliminate other threats to his wellbeing, such, for example, as the one caused by the present explosive rate of human reproduction—a threat considered by some to be far more menacing in the long run than H-bombs and bacterial warfare (Cf. C. G. Darwin, 1953). Yet the record of man's evolutionary accomplishments, together with the fact that his knowledge, sense of responsibility, and goodwill have the power to increase, provide grounds for hope. Would it not be strange if, after so many millennia, man should suddenly come to the end of his tether in the twentieth century? Would it not be even stranger if, with the possibilities opened up by man's appearance in the evolutionary scheme, the ascent of life should end?

BIBLIOGRAPHY

Only works cited in the text are listed

AGAR, W. E. 1943. *A Contribution to the Theory of the Living Organism*. Melbourne, University Press.

ALLEE, W. C., A. E. EMERSON, O. PARK, T. PARK and K. P. SCHMIDT. 1949. *Principles of Animal Ecology*. Philadelphia, Saunders.

ALLEE, W. C. 1951. *The Social Life of Animals*. Revised ed. Boston, Beacon Press; London, Pitman.

BARFIELD, O. 1957. *Saving the Appearances*. London, Faber.

BATESON, W. 1914. Inaugural Address to the Australian meeting of the British Association for the Advancement of Science. *Nature*, XCIII, 635-42.

BERG, L. S. 1926. *Nomogenesis; or Evolution Determined by Law*. Tr. from the Russian by J. N. Rostovtsow. London, Constable.

BERGSON, H. 1911. *Creative Evolution*. Tr. from the French by A. Mitchell. London, Macmillan.

BERGSON, H. 1919. *L'Energie Spirituelle; Essais et Conférences*. Paris, Alcan.

BERNAL, J. D. 1951. *The Physical Basis of Life*. London, Routledge and Kegan Paul.

BERTALANFFY, L. VON. 1950. 'The Theory of Open Systems in Physics and Biology'. *Science*, III, 23-9.

BERTALANFFY, L. VON. 1952. *Problems of Life*. New York, Wiley; London, Watts.

BLUM, H. F. 1951. *Time's Arrow and Evolution* (2nd ed. with revisions, 1955). Princeton University Press.

BLUM, H. F. 1955. 'Perspectives in Evolution'. *American Scientist*, 43, 595-610.

BOLK, L. 1926. *Das Problem der Menschenwerdung*. Jena, Fischer.

BONDI, H. 1952. *Cosmology*. Cambridge University Press.

BRAITHWAITE, R. B. 1953. *Scientific Explanation*. Cambridge University Press.

BROAD, C. D. 1923. *Scientific Thought*, London, Kegan Paul.

BROAD, C. D. 1925. *The Mind and its Place in Nature*. London, Kegan Paul.

BROOM, R. 1933. 'Evolution—Is There Intelligence Behind It?' *South African Journal of Science*, XXX, 1-19.

BURMA, B. H. 1949. 'The Species Concept: A Semantic Review'. *Evolution*, III, 369-73.

CANNON, H. G. 1958. *The Evolution of Living Things*. Manchester University Press.

CARTER, G. S. 1951. *Animal Evolution; A Study of Recent Views of its Causes*. London, Sidgwick and Jackson.

CARTER, G. S. 1957. *A Hundred Years of Evolution*. London, Sidgwick and Jackson.

CHILDE, V. G. 1941. *Man Makes Himself*. The Thinker's Library. London, Watts.

CHILDE, V. G., 1951. *Social Evolution*. London, Watts.

CLARK, A. H. 1930. *The New Evolution, Zoögenesis*. Baltimore, Williams.

COLLINGWOOD, R. G. 1946. *The Idea of History*. Oxford University Press.

CUENOT, L. 1921. *La Genèse des Espèces Animales*. Paris, Felix Alcan.

CUENOT, L. 1941. *Invention et finalité en biologie*. Paris, Flammarion.

CUENOT, L. 1951. *L'Evolution biologique, les faits, les incertitudes*. Paris, Masson (with the collaboration of A. Tetry).

DALCQ, A. M. 1951. 'Le problème de l'évolution: est-il près d'être resolu?' *Annales de la Société Royal Zoologique de Belgique*, 82, 117-38.

DARWIN, C. 1859. *On the Origin of Species by Means of Natural Selection, or the preservation of favoured races in the struggle for life*. London, Murray.

DARWIN, C. G. 1953. *The Next Million Years*. New York, Doubleday; London, Hart-Davis.

DARWIN, C. G. 1956. Remarks in a Symposium, 'The Unstable Equilibrium of Man in Nature', in *Man's Rôle in Changing the Face of the Earth*. Ed. W. L. Thomas, Jr. Chicago, Wenner-Gren Foundation.

DAVIS, D. D. 1949. 'Comparative Anatomy and the Evolution of the Vertebrates' in *Genetics, Paleontology, and Evolution*. Eds. G. L. Jepsen, E. Mayr, G. G. Simpson. Princeton University Press.

DE BEER, G. R. 1951. 'Genetics and Embryology' in *A Century of Science*. Ed. H. Dingle. London, Hutchinson.

DECUGIS, H. 1941. *Le vieillissement du monde vivant*. Paris, Masson.

DOBZHANSKY, TH. 1950a. 'Heredity, Environment, and Evolution', *Science*, III, 161-6.

DOBZHANSKY, TH. 1950b. 'Evolution in the Tropics'. *American Scientist*, 28, 209-11.

DOBZHANSKY, TH. 1951. *Genetics and the Origin of Species*. 3rd Edition revised. New York, Columbia University Press; Oxford University Press.

DOBZHANSKY, TH. 1955. *Evolution, Genetics and Man*. New York, Wiley; London, Chapman and Hall.

DOBZHANSKY, TH. 1956. *The Biological Basis of Human Freedom*. New York, Columbia University Press; Oxford University Press.

DOBZHANSKY, TH. 1958. 'Evolution at Work', *Science*, 127, 1091-8.

DRIESCH, H. 1908. *Science and Philosophy of the Organism*. London, Macmillan.

DRUMMOND, H. 1894. *The Ascent of Man*. London, Hodder and Stoughton.

'ESPINASSE, P. G. 1952. 'Selection of the Genetic Basis for an Acquired Character'. *Nature*, 170, 71.

EVANS, J. L. 1953. 'On Meaning and Verification', *Mind*, LXII, 1-19.

FISHER, R. A. 1930. *The Genetical Theory of Natural Selection*. Oxford, Clarendon Press.

FORD, E. B. 1949. *Mendelism and Evolution*. 5th ed. London, Methuen.

FRANK, L. K., HUTCHINSON, G. E., LIVINGSTONE, W. K., McCULLOCH, W. S., and N. WIENER. 1948. 'Teleological Mechanisms'. *Annals of the New York Academy of Sciences*, 50, 189-277.

GILMOUR, J. S. L. and J. W. GREGOR. 1939. 'Demes: A Suggested New Terminology', *Nature*, 144, 333.

GILMOUR, J. S. L. 1940. 'Taxonomy and Philosophy' in *The New Systematics*, Ed. J. S. Huxley. Oxford, Clarendon Press.

GINSBERG, M. 1944. 'Moral Progress'. Frazer Lecture at the University of Glasgow. Glasgow University Press.

GOLDSCHMIDT, R. B. 1940. *The Material Basis of Evolution*. New Haven, Yale University Press.

GOLDSCHMIDT, R. B. 1952. 'Evolution as viewed by one Geneticist', *American Scientist*, 40, 84-98.

GOLDSCHMIDT, R. B. 1953. 'An Introduction to a Popularized Symposium on Evolution', *Scientific Monthly*, 67, 183-4.

HALDANE, J. B. S. 1927. *Possible Worlds*. London, Chatto and Windus.

HALDANE, J. B. S. 1932a. *The Causes of Evolution*. New York, Harper; London, Longmans.

HALDANE, J. B. S. 1932b. 'The Hereditary Transmission of Acquired Characters', *Nature*, 79, 817, 856; 80, 20, 204.

HALDANE, J. B. S. 1949. 'Human Evolution: Past and Future', in *Genetics, Paleontology, and Evolution*. Eds. G. L. Jepsen, E. Mayr, G. G. Simpson. Princeton University Press.

HALDANE, J. B. S. 1954a. 'The Origin of Life', *New Biology*, 16, 12-27.

HALDANE, J. B. S. 1954b. 'The Statics of Evolution', in *Evolution as a Process*. Eds. J. S. Huxley, A. C. Hardy, E. B. Ford. London, Allen and Unwin, 109-21.

HANSON, N. R. 1955. 'Causal Chains', *Mind*, 64, 289-311.

HAYEK, F. A. 1955. 'Degrees of Explanation', *The British Journal for the Philosophy of Science*, 6, 209-25.

HELMER, O. and RESCHER, N. 1959. 'On the Epistemology of the Inexact Sciences'. *Management Science*, 6, 25-52.

P

HEMPEL, C. G. 1951. 'The Concept of Cognitive Significance', *Proceedings of the American Academy of Arts and Sciences*, 80, 61-75.

HEMPEL, C. G. 1952. *Fundamentals of Concept Formation in Empirical Science*. International Encyclopedia of Unified Science, II, 7. Chicago, University of Chicago Press.

HENDERSON, L. J. 1913. *The Fitness of the Environment*. New York, Macmillan.

HENDERSON, L. J. 1917. *The Order of Nature*. Cambridge, Mass., Harvard University Press.

HERRICK, C. J. 1956. *The Evolution of Human Nature*. Austin, University of Texas Press.

HRDLICKA, A. 1942. 'The Problem of Human Evolution', in *Science and Man*. Ed. R. N. Anshen. New York, Harcourt.

HUXLEY, JULIAN S. 1932. *Problems of Relative Growth*. London, Methuen.

HUXLEY, JULIAN S. 1941. *Man Stands Alone*. New York, Harper.

HUXLEY, JULIAN S. 1942. *Evolution; The Modern Synthesis*. London, Allen and Unwin.

HUXLEY, JULIAN S. 1943. *Evolutionary Ethics*. Romanes Lecture. Oxford University Press.

HUXLEY, JULIAN S. 1949. *Heredity; East and West*. New York, Harper.

HUXLEY, JULIAN S. 1951. 'Genetics, Evolution and Human Destiny' in *Genetics in the Twentieth Century*. Ed. L. C. Dunn. New York, Macmillan.

HUXLEY, JULIAN S. 1953. *Evolution in Action*. London, Chatto and Windus.

HUXLEY, JULIAN S. 1957. *Religion Without Revelation*. London, Parrish.

JEPSEN, G. L. 1949. 'Selection, "Orthogenesis" and the Fossil Record', *Proceedings of the American Philosophical Society*, 93, 479-500.

KROPOTKIN, P. 1902. *Mutual Aid*. New York, McClure Phillips (1914, Knopf).

LERNER, I. M. 1950. *Population Genetics and Animal Improvement*. Cambridge University Press.

LERNER, I. M. 1958. *The Genetical Basis of Selection*. New York, Wiley.

LEWIS, G. N. 1926. *The Anatomy of Science*. New Haven, Yale University Press.

LINDSEY, A. W. 1952. *Principles of Organic Evolution*. St Louis, Mosby.

LOTKA, A. J. 1944. 'Evolution and Thermodynamics', *Science and Society*, 8, 161-71

LOTKA, A. J. 1945. 'The Law of Evolution as a Maximal Principle', *Human Biology*, 17, 167-94.

LULL, R. S. 1929. *Organic Evolution*. New York, Macmillan; London, Macmillan.

MACBRIDE, E. W. 1932. 'The Inheritance of Acquired Characters', *Nature*, 130, 128.

MAINX, F. 1954. *Foundations of Biology*. International Encyclopedia of Unified Science, I, 9. Chicago, University of Chicago Press.

MARTIN, C. P. 1953. 'A Non-Geneticist Looks at Evolution', *American Scientist*, 41, 100-5

MARTIN, C. P. 1957. *Psychology, Evolution and Sex*. Oxford, Blackwell.

MAYR, E. 1942. *Systematics and the Origin of Species*. New York, Columbia University Press.

MAYR, E. 1949a. 'Speciation and Selection', *Proceedings of the American Philosophical Society*, 93, 514-19.

MAYR, E. 1949b. 'Speciation and Systematics', in *Genetics, Paleontology, and Evolution*. Eds. G. L. Jepsen, E. Mayr, G. G. Simpson. Princeton University Press.

MCGILVARY, E. B. 1956. *Toward a Perspective Realism*. La Salle, Ind. Open Court.

MEDAWAR, P. B. 1951. 'Zoology' in *Scientific Thought in the Twentieth Century*. Ed. A. E. Heath. London, Watts.

MEDAWAR, P. B. 1957. *The Uniqueness of the Individual*. London, Methuen.

MEHLBERG, H. 1958. *The Reach of Science*. Toronto, University of Toronto Press.

MILLER, H. 1949. *The Community of Man*. New York, Macmillan.

MONTAGU, A. 1952. *Darwin, Competition and Co-operation*. New York, Schuman.

MOODY, P. A. 1953. *Introduction to Evolution*. New York, Harper.

MULLER, H. J. 1929a. 'The Gene as the Basis of Life', *Proceedings of the International Congress of Plant Sciences*, 1, 897-921.

MULLER, H. J. 1929b. 'The Method of Evolution', *Scientific Monthly*, 29, 481-505.

MULLER, H. J. 1939. 'Reversibility in Evolution Considered from the Standpoint of Genetics', *Biological Review*, 14, 261-80.

MULLER, H. J. 1949. 'The Darwinian and Modern Conception of Natural Selection', *Proceedings of the American Philosophical Society*, 93, 459-70.

MULLER, H. J. 1957. 'Man's Place in Living Nature', *Scientific Monthly*, 84, 245-54.

MULLER, H. J. 1958. 'Evolution by Mutation', *Bulletin of the American Mathematical Association*, 64, 137-60.

NEEDHAM, J. 1943. *Time: The Refreshing River*. London, Allen and Unwin.

NEEDHAM, J. 1946. *History is on Our Side*. London, Allen and Unwin.

NEWMAN, H. H. 1936. *Outlines of General Zoology*. 3rd Ed. Chicago, University of Chicago Press.

O'CONNOR, D. J. 1957. 'Determinism and Predictability', *The British Journal for the Philosophy of Science*, 7, 310-15.

PANTIN, C. F. A 1951. 'Organic Design', *British Association for the Advancement of Science*, 8, 138-49.

PEIRCE, C. S. 1931-5. *Collected Papers*. Eds. C. Hartshorne and P. Weiss, 6 vols. Cambridge, Harvard University Press; Oxford University Press.

PITTENDRIGH, C. S. 1958. 'Adaptation, Natural Selection and Behaviour', in *Behaviour and Evolution*. Ed. G. G. Simpson and A. Roe. New Haven, Yale University Press.

POPPER, K. R. 1956. 'Three Views Concerning Human Knowledge' in *Contemporary British Philosophy*. Ed. H. D. Lewis. III. London, Allen and Unwin.

POPPER, K. R. 1957a. 'Philosophy of Science : A Personal Report' in *British Philosophy in the Mid-century*. Ed. C. A. Mace. Allen and Unwin.

POPPER, K. R. 1957b. *The Poverty of Historicism*. London, Routledge and Kegan Paul.

POPPER, K. R. 1959. *The Logic of Scientific Discovery*. London, Hutchinson.

RAVEN, C. E. 1953. *Natural Religion and Christian Theology*. Cambridge University Press.

RENSCH, B. 1947. *Neuere Probleme der Abstammungslehre, die transspezifische Evolution*. Stuttgart, Enke.

RENSCH, B. 1954. 'Relation between the Evolution of Central Nervous Functions and the Body Size of Animals', in *Evolution as a Process*. Ed. J. S. Huxley, A. C. Hardy, E. B. Ford. London, Allen and Unwin, 181-200.

RESCHER, N. 1958. 'A Theory of Evidence'. *Philosophy of Science*, 25, 83-94.

RITCHIE, J. 1940. 'Perspectives in Evolution', *Annual Report for the Smithsonian Institution for 1940*, Washington, D.C., 249-69.

ROMER, A. S. 1941. *Man and the Vertebrates*. 3rd ed. Chicago, University of Chicago Press.

ROMER, A. S. 1949. 'Time-Series and Trends in Animal Evolution' in *Genetics, Paleontology and Evolution*. Eds. G. L. Jepsen, E. Mayr, G. G. Simpson. Princeton University Press.

ROSTAND, J. 1951. *Les grand courants de la biologie*. Paris, Galliard.

ROSTAND, J. 1956. *A Biologist's View*. London, Heinemann.

RUSSELL, B. 1927. *An Outline of Philosophy*. London, Allen and Unwin.

RUSSELL, E. S. 1945. *The Directiveness of Organic Activities*. Cambridge University Press.

RYLE, G. 1949. *The Concept of Mind*. London, Hutchinson.

SCHEFFLER, I. 1957. 'Explanation, Prediction and Abstraction', *The British Journal for the Philosophy of Science*, 7, 310-15.

SCHINDEWOLF, O. H. 1936. *Paleontologie, Entwicklungslehre und Genetik*. Berlin, Borntraeger.

SCHRODINGER, E. 1945. *What is Life?* Cambridge University Press.

SCHRODINGER, E. 1954. *Nature and the Greeks*. Cambridge University Press.

SCHRODINGER, E. 1958. *Mind and Matter*. Cambridge University Press.

SCRIVEN, M. 1959. 'Explanation and Prediction in Evolutionary Theory'. *Science*, 130, 477-82.

SHERRINGTON, C. 1953. *Man On His Nature*. 2nd Edition. New York, Doubleday [Anchor Book, 15]; Cambridge University Press.

SIMPSON, G. G. 1944. *Tempo and Mode in Evolution*. New York, Columbia University Press; Oxford University Press.

SIMPSON, G. G. 1945. 'The Principles of Classification and a Classification of Mammals'. *Bulletin of the American Museum of Natural History*, 85, 1-350.

SIMPSON, G. G. 1947. 'The Problem of Plan and Purpose in Nature', *Scientific Monthly*, 64, 481-95.

SIMPSON, G. G. 1949. *The Meaning of Evolution*. New Haven, Yale University Press; Oxford University Press.

SIMPSON, G. G. 1950a. 'Evolutionary Determinism and the Fossil Record', *Scientific Monthly*, 71, 262-7.

SIMPSON, G. G. 1950b. Art. 'Evolution' in *Chambers's Encyclopaedia*, London.

SIMPSON, G. G. 1953. *The Major Features of Evolution*. New York, Columbia University Press; Oxford University Press.

SIMPSON, G. G., C. S. PITTENDRIGH and L. H. TIFFANY. 1957. *Life, An Introduction to Biology*. New York, Harcourt Brace.

SINNOTT, E. W. 1950. *Cell and Psyche: the Biology of Purpose*. Chapel Hill, University of North Carolina Press.

SMITH, J. M. 1958. *The Theory of Evolution*. Harmondsworth, Eng. Penguin Books.

SONNEBORN, T. M. 1951. 'Beyond the Gene—Two Years Later', in *Science Progress*, 7th Series. New Haven, Yale University Press.

STADLER, L. J. 1954. 'The Gene', *Science*, 120, 811-19.

STEBBINS, G. L. 1950. *Variation and Evolution in Plants*. New York, Columbia University Press; Oxford University Press.

STERN, C. 1953. 'The Geneticist's Analysis of the Material and the Means of Evolution', *Scientific Monthly*, 77, 190-7.
STRAUS, W. L. 1949. 'The Riddle of Man's Ancestry', *The Quarterly Review of Biology*, 24, 200-23.
TEILHARD DE CHARDIN, P. 1955-7. *Oeuvres*. 3 vols. Paris, Editions du Seuil.
TEILHARD DE CHARDIN, P. 1956. 'The Antiquity and World-Expansion of Human Culture', in *Man's Rôle in Changing the Face of the Earth*. Ed. W. L. Thomas, Jr. Chicago, Wenner-Gren Foundation.
THODAY, J. M. 1953. 'Components of Fitness', *Symposia of the Society for Experimental Biology*, 7 (Evolution), 96-113.
THODAY, J. M. 1958. 'Natural Selection and Biological Progress' in *A Century of Darwin*. Ed. S. A. Barnett. London, Heinemann.
UMBGROVE, J. H. F. 1950. *Symphony of the Earth*. The Hague, Martinus Nijhoff.
VANDEL, A. 1949. *L'homme et l'évolution*. Paris, Gallimard.
WADDINGTON, C. H. 1939. *An Introduction to Modern Genetics*. New York, Macmillan; London, Allen and Unwin.
WADDINGTON, C. H. 1942. 'The Epigenotype', *Endeavour*, I, 18-20.
WADDINGTON, C. H. 1953. 'Epigenetics and Evolution', *Symposia of the Society for Experimental Biology*, 7 (Evolution), 186-99.
WAISMANN, F. 1945. 'Verifiability', *Proceedings of the Aristotelian Society*, Sup., Vol. XIX, 119-50.
WELLS, H. G., HUXLEY, J. S. and WELLS, G. P. 1931. *The Science of Life*. New York, Doubleday. Two vols.
WHITEHEAD, A. N. 1929. *Science and the Modern World*. New York, Macmillan; Cambridge University Press.
WHYTE, L. L. 1954. *Accent on Form*. New York, Harper; London, Routledge.
WIENER, N. 1948. *Cybernetics*. New York, Wiley.
WILLIS, J. C. 1940. *The Course of Evolution*. Cambridge University Press.
WITTGENSTEIN, L. 1953. *Philosophical Investigations*. Oxford, Blackwell.
WOODGER, J. H. 1929. *Biological Principles*. London, Routledge, Kegan Paul.
WOOD-JONES, F. 1953. *Trends of Life*. London, Arnold.
WRIGHT, S. 1932. 'The Rôles of Mutation, Inbreeding, Crossbreeding and Selection in Evolution', *Proceedings of the Sixth International Congress of Genetics*, I, 356-66.
WRIGHT, S. 1945. 'Tempo and Mode in Evolution : A Critical Review', *Ecology*, 26, 415-19.
WRIGHT, S. 1948. 'On the Rôles of Directed and Random Changes in the Genetics of Populations', *Evolution*, II, 279-94.

WRIGHT, S. 1949. 'Population Structure in Evolution', *Proceedings of the American Philosophical Society*, 93, 471-8.

WRIGHT, S. 1952. Art. 'Evolution' in *Encyclopaedia Britannica*, 1952 edition. Vol. 8. Chicago and London.

WRIGHT, S. 1956. 'Modes of Selection', *The American Naturalist*, 90, 5-24.

YOUNG, J. Z. 1957. *The Life of Mammals*. Oxford, Clarendon.

ZEUNER, F. A. 1946. *Dating the Past*. London, Methuen.

INDEX OF NAMES

INDEX OF SUBJECTS